Dr Brenda Lintner BA, MRCP (Ed,,
specialised in psychiatry for more years than she cares to recall. She has written on psychiatric topics, lectured extensively to community groups and has recently published a book *Living with Schizophrenia* in the Positive Health Guide Series. She has worked as a consultant psychiatrist in this country, spending some time in child psychiatry, and in America and Canada where she lectured at the University of Calgary. She now works as an independent psychiatrist and is an active medical member of the Mental Health Review Tribunals whose function it is to monitor the criteria for compulsory detention of psychiatric patients of all ages.

Dr Lintner has always been specially interested in the problems of young people and holds the view that appropriate and wise intervention in the early years may help to alleviate much psychiatric morbidity in later life.

She can lay claim to a personal experience of teenagers since her son, to whom this book is dedicated, is now in his early twenties. He would deny that he was anything other than a model teenager.

O P T I M A

LIVING WITH TEENAGERS

Dr Brenda Lintner

POSITIVE HEALTH GUIDE

For Matthew, who gave me many ideas.

© Dr Brenda Lintner 1991

First published in 1991 by
Macdonald Optima, a division of
Macdonald & Co. (Publishers) Ltd

A member of Maxwell Macmillan Pergamon Publishing Corporation

British Library Cataloguing in Publication Data
Lintner, Brenda
    Living with teenagers. — (Positive health guide)
    1. Adolescents
    I. Title   II. Series
    305.2355

    ISBN 0–356–19117–6

Macdonald & Co. (Publishers) Ltd
Orbit House
1 New Fetter Lane
London EC4A 1AR

Typeset in Times by Leaper & Gard Ltd, Bristol

Printed and bound in Great Britain by
Mackays of Chatham PLC, Chatham, Kent

CONTENTS

PREFACE

I realised as I began to write this book that I had taken on a somewhat daunting task. I also appreciated that, for many parents in our present society, the growing up of their children can create anxieties alongside the pleasures of seeing them become adults.

My book is not intended to be a manual for parenthood, but a guide which parents can consult, as and when necessary.

In a work of this length, it is impossible to go into great detail about every problem, but the counselling services listed at the end produce practical leaflets which will be extremely helpful.

The views expressed are entirely my own, based upon my experience as a parent and as a doctor who has always been particularly interested in teenage problems. Parents are naturally free to disagree with them, but there is one fact that we must all acknowledge. Communication between a child and their parents starts at the beginning of life and should be a continuous process. If your children feel free to talk to you when they are young, they will feel much more able to carry this on, not only into adolescence, but into adult life as well, something which can be one of life's richest experiences.

1

NORMAL ADOLESCENT DEVELOPMENT

PHYSIOLOGICAL CHANGES OF PUBERTY

Adolescence can be most appropriately defined as the period between childhood and adult maturity. It is initiated by the hormonal activity of puberty, the onset of which is variable, being at the average age of 9–13 for girls and 10–15 for boys. At puberty, there is growth and maturation of the sex organs, secondary sexual characteristics develop, and sexual fertility is attained.

Sex is determined at conception by the matching of the sex chromosomes, an XX distribution producing a girl and an XY distribution a boy.

In girls, puberty is heralded by breast development, the appearance of pubic hair and a spurt of growth over a period of about eighteen months. The onset of the monthly periods (menstruation) does not occur until after the peak of the growth spurt has passed and breast and pubic hair growth are well advanced.

In boys, however, the development of pubic hair and penile and testicular enlargement precedes the growth spurt and is then followed by sperm production and the ability to ejaculate seminal fluid.

In both sexes puberty commences when the pituitary gland, an endocrine hormone-secreting organ at the base of the brain, begins to secrete increasingly large quantities of *gonadotrophins*, which are hormones or chemical messengers, which act upon the ovaries or testicles. Such gonadotrophins are secreted from the time of intrauterine life throughout childhood, but it appears to be the sudden increase in their strength which is responsible for the onset of puberty. Presumably, the age at which

1

such an increase occurs is in some way imprinted into the species, since the onset of sexual development is substantially delayed in humans as compared with other mammals. The pituitary also produces a growth-stimulating hormone which is required for growth in height and in bone mass, bone maturation, and for the complex chemical processes which are essential for normal bodily development.

The pituitary acts in collaboration with the hypothalamus, an adjacent organ in the centre of the brain. The hypothalamus produces hormones which act upon the pituitary so that it is stimulated to secrete its gonadotrophins and growth hormone. Thus, it is obvious that disturbances within either the hypothalamus or the pituitary gland can produce delays in the onset of puberty.

There are two types of gonadotrophin hormone. The first is *luteinising* hormone (LH) which causes the cells in the ovaries to commence producing the female hormone *oestradiol* and those in the testes to produce the male hormone *testosterone*. The second is the *follicle-stimulating hormone* (FSH) which increases oestradiol and testosterone production. Thus the mechanism of sexual development can be seen as a constant circle of interactions between the hypothalamic–pituitary complex and the sexual organs. It is the secretion of testosterone from the testes and oestradiol from the ovaries that is responsible for the major physical changes of puberty.

Secretions of *thyroxine* hormone from the thyroid gland play an important part in growth and in the correct functioning of all bodily organs. Lack of this hormone leads to an impairment of both physical and mental development.

The adrenal glands produce *steroids* involved in muscular development and general metabolism and sex hormones called *androgens* which act with oestradiol and testosterone in producing the secondary sexual characteristics such as body hair, distribution of body fat, and voice deepening in boys.

The onset of the menstrual cycle in girls is characterised by the development of one of the many follicles contained in the ovaries under the influence of FSH from the pituitary. The follicle produces oestradiol which, by a feedback mechanism, reduces FSH production. A consequent surge of LH from the pituitary induces the release of an egg (ovum) from the follicle – ovulation – which occurs roughly in the middle of the menstrual cycle and which is, therefore, the time of maximum fertility. After the ovum has been released, the remaining cells of the follicle form a yellow body called the *corpus luteum*, which secretes oestradiol, and another hormone called *proges-*

terone. The latter plays an important part in preparing the lining of the womb for a pregnancy. If, however, the ovum is not fertilised, the corpus luteum disintegrates, the level of hormone it produces falls and, since the lining of the womb (endometrium) is not getting enough hormonal support, it is shed as a menstrual bleed. Then the cycle recommences. It has been shown that menstrual periods are not regularly associated with ovulation for the first two years after the menarche (onset of menstruation), so consequently the cycles may be irregular during this time. It follows that full fertility is not established until there is regular ovulation.

In contrast, production of spermatozoa in the male is a continuous process and it appears that male fertility is established once the testes have developed and spermatogenesis is taking place.

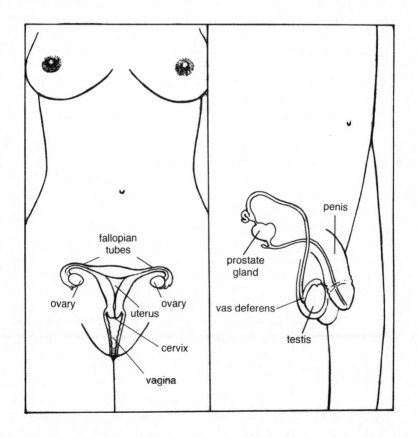

REASONS FOR DELAYED PUBERTY

There is a considerable variation in the onset of puberty, probably related to genetic, nutritional, and environmental factors. Fortunately, significant delay is comparatively rare and in most adolescents the endocrine changes, once begun, proceed smoothly and in an orderly sequence. Ninety-seven per cent of boys and girls show signs of pubertal development by their fourteenth birthday. A testicular volume of 4 mls measured using an orchidometer indicates the onset of male puberty. The first sign of female puberty is the enlargement of the breast bud. There are a number of factors, however, which can delay normal sexual development and parents should seek advice if puberty is delayed after the age of 14 in either sex.

The child is a late developer

This is the commonest cause of delayed puberty. Under these circumstances there is likely to be delayed growth as well as delayed puberty, since the two factors go together. An assessment of growth rate has to be made, ideally by the same person over a minimum interval of three to four months. No further action needs to be taken if the growth rate is proceeding normally, since pubertal development can be expected within a short space of time.

Nutritional factors

Undernutrition can retard growth rate and delay puberty. It can occur in children with diabetes who have a problem with their diet control, or in those with a severe metabolic disorder such as coeliac disease or fibrocystic disease of the pancreas, where there is interference with adequate food utilisation. Severe asthma or heart disease may have a similar effect.

Psychological factors

Serious emotional deprivation can delay puberty. Emotional upsets can also produce amenorrhoea (absence of periods which have been established). In the condition of anorexia nervosa, which will be discussed in Chapter 4, psychological and nutritional factors combine to produce either delayed puberty or amenorrhoea.

Glandular disorder

Any failure of the complex system of hypothalamus, pituitary, ovaries, testes, and/or adrenals can be responsible for delayed puberty and is associated with delayed growth measured over a period of time, thus being distinguished from late development. Such conditions should always be the subject of specialist advice, so that levels of hormone secretion can be ascertained and treatment with appropriate hormones given. Ultrasound techniques can be used to determine the size and appearance of the ovaries and uterus in girls and for locating intra-abdominal testes in boys.

In boys it is important to establish that the testes have descended into the scrotum since, if they remain in the intra-abdominal cavity, the consequent body heat interferes with spermatogenesis. Failure of one testicle to descend can occur as a minor developmental abnormality and should be treated in childhood by an operation to place it in its proper position in the scrotum. Bilateral undescended testicles are much more rare and are more likely to indicate a hormonal problem, since it is unlikely that a developmental abnormality will occur on both sides. Such a condition requires detailed analysis of hormonal functioning at a specialist centre and operative treatment to reposition the testicles.

Chromosomal abnormalities

Rarely, there is a disorder in the constitution of the chromosomes, those bodies within living cells which carry the genes that give each individual their unique quality. Usually, there are associated physical abnormalities which make the diagnosis clear. The individual's genetic constitution can be ascertained by means of chromosomal karotyping. Examination of a piece of skin or a blood cell, for example, will reveal the appearance (size, shape, and number) of chromosomes. In certain conditions associated with delayed puberty there is an absence of one X chromosome in girls, an extra X chromosome in boys, or some other type of chromosomal abnormality. These will also require specialist assessment and treatment.

PSYCHOLOGICAL CHANGES IN ADOLESCENCE

The essential feature of the adolescent period is the change from the dependence of the child to the independence of the adult, and it would appear that the more sophisticated and demanding a society, the greater the degree of conflict this development causes. In less developed societies the passage from child to adult can be marked quite definitely by initiation ceremonies; the child has a fixed point at which they are expected to take part in the adult world, and marriages are arranged as

5

soon as sexual development takes place. In effect the adolescent, unless particularly rebellious, is not left with many choices.

In Western society the period of adolescence is now prolonged, and there are often no effective guidelines and a vast number of choices which it is possible to make. Moreover, since adolescence is a natural progression from childhood, a number of adolescents start this period of their life with educational, emotional, and social disadvantages which increase the problem of their growing up.

INCREASED INTEREST IN THE BODY IMAGE

This is one of the universal changes in adolescence. A child normally takes a limited interest in appearance, but the obvious changes of puberty and the awakening awareness of the opposite sex leads to preoccupation with looks, weight, height, and so on. The teenager may feel too fat or too thin, worry about the size of the breasts or penis, and be preoccupied with minor skin blemishes. A mild degree of *acne* may be treated by careful skin cleansing and antiseptic lotions. Severe acne can be extremely distressing at a time when appearance is important, but it can be treated by the use of antibiotic tablets, particularly tetracyclines or Erythromycin given under medical supervision.

It is important that the adolescent should be made to feel attractive and to be reassured that they are developing normally. Since they are frequently hypersensitive, they should not be teased about their spots or their weight, particularly in front of other people, and should not be the subject of unkind comparisons with their peers. Perhaps the ultimate in how to give a teenager a complex was a father who insisted that he could not walk on the pavement with his mildly overweight daughter.

It becomes important for them to be accepted by their peer group. One should, therefore, try to accept calmly the experiments that a teenager may make with their appearance – the black lipstick and eye-shadow, shiny green nail varnish, red and purple hair-streaks – since they may well decide for themselves after a while that they do not like them. However, one should equally try to help them avoid altering their appearance in a way which cannot afterwards be easily changed. Tattoos are probably the best example of this. Some boys, in particular, get tattooed in a moment of bravado, only to discover that it is extremely difficult to have the marks removed. Moreover, if strict standards of hygiene are not applied, the needles used are a potential source of infection.

Embarrassment about pubertal development can often be traced back to sexual inhibitions reinforced in childhood. Some girls try to hide their developing breasts in loose clothing and become positively round-shouldered. Boys are distressed by the appearance of facial hair and deepening of the voice. As in all other aspects of adolescence, the seeds sown in childhood are vital. If sexuality has always been the subject of taboos, this will be carried on into adolescent attitudes. Both sexes should be encouraged to regard puberty as a time to which they can look forward as the beginning of a rewarding adult life.

EMOTIONAL LABILITY

Sudden swings of mood and attitude are common to all adolescents, not surprisingly, in view of the profound hormonal changes that are taking place. The mood may alternate between a return to childish dependence or demonstrative affection and sulkiness or argumentative defiance. In order to become an adult, the adolescent has to establish their own identity, exert their independence and see their parents as vulnerable human beings with faults and failings. It is essential that parents should try to preserve their equanimity during this period, hard though it may sometimes be. In this respect, one-parent families can be at a disadvantage if there is no adult person in whom they can confide. On the other hand, there won't be any fierce arguments which can affect the child.

It is wise, however, to avoid allowing transient teenage behaviour to put you in the wrong. It may be tempting to feel that it must be something that you have said that leads your teenager to arrive from school, scowling, and to retire to their room, banging the door without saying a word. This behaviour is just as likely to be due to a variety of other reasons, such as problems at school, and teenagers need parents to remain calm and in control in what can be, for them, a very uncertain world. It is important, though, to pick a time when the teenager is more accessible to ask them what it was that had upset them, since it may be some important matter that they would really like to discuss and do not know how to approach. This is particularly so where parents have set excessively high standards and the teenagers feel that they have failed to live up to their expectations.

QUESTIONING OF ADULT VALUES

This is another essential part of adolescence and is vital for future development. It may be irritating or even upsetting to be called 'an old reactionary' or to be told that you have 'middle-class values of acquiring property and money' by the teenager for whose future you are making sacrifices. As an adult, however, it is all too easy to slip into a complacent acceptance of the status quo or into an uncritical reiteration of long-cherished beliefs. If we are wise we should reappraise our attitudes all the time, and the challenge of a teenager helps us do this.

An adolescent should be treated as an adult and their arguments answered with a reasoned reply. Be prepared to see things from their point of view and accept that either of you may be able to convince the other or agree to differ. Never fall back upon the argument that 'when you get to my age you will change' or 'you are too young to understand'. Neither of these statements is necessarily true and, in any case, makes no sense to the teenager, who is seeing the world through new and different eyes. Moreover, teenagers will sometimes advance arguments because they want to test out the sincerity and logicality of your opinions and because they wish to clarify their own feelings about a topic. The parents and children who are most likely to establish a strong adult relationship are those who have been able to talk freely about any topic during the adolescent period.

DEFIANCE AND REBELLION

Defiance and rebellion are a natural part of an adolescent's need to become independent as an adult. A teenager who is excessively compliant may well seem easy to handle at the time, but often proceeds into adult life with a childish dependence upon the parents, which makes the establishment of mature relationships with others difficult. They become the people who, even if they marry, cannot bear to move away from their parents or rely upon them excessively to solve any minor difficulty. This naturally is not beneficial to their marriage or encouraging to their partner.

Some parents, who feel a need to have their children remain like Peter Pans for the rest of their life, encourage this, usually unconsciously, by making the adolescent feel afraid of the outside world as a very threatening place. They have to be taken everywhere by their parents, go out with them rather than their own friends, and are the recipients of warnings about how their friends of either sex are likely to try to exploit them. This process is frequently only a continuation of overprotectiveness in childhood, which serves to make the teenager timid, nervous, and shy, or, more rarely, actively rebellious. Often this occurs when the parents themselves have little outside satisfaction, other than in their parental roles. Just as teenagers need to establish themselves as independent beings, so parents have to develop their own interests and look forward to a time when they cease to have to look after a dependant.

On the other hand, parents who take no interest in their teenagers produce just as many problems. The evidence is that adolescents need a caring and structured environment and that they become bewildered if their parents do not care whether or not they attend school or if they stay out all night and with whom. Although teenagers may complain that their parents are 'too strict', it is worse if they do not appear to care at all. Teenagers are not unique in this respect, as witness a patient of mine who, having nerved herself to tell her husband about an extramarital affair, felt she might murder him when he told her that her confession must wait until the end of 'Match of the Day'.

It is important, in my opinion, that parents should set a standard of behaviour for their children. By this I do not mean that they should impose upon the youngsters all their own beliefs and opinions. However, it appears that adolescents feel safer when they know that there are some ground rules. Thus, parents should expect them to attend school, study to their maximum ability, put their all into any occupation they take up, avoid exploiting others in their relationships, and shun criminal activities.

If your child is not attending school or cannot hold down a job, then this should be a matter for discussion between you with a view to remedying the situation. There is no point in conniving at an escape route by, for example, writing sick notes or blaming the teachers or the employers. It may well be that the problems are on both sides, but to allow a teenager to think that they can escape from life's difficulties by illness is only to encourage a carryover of this attitude into adult life. A parent should try to ascertain exactly what is happening and then help their child to do something positive about it. Thus, if a teenager is refusing to go to school because of bullying, a whole range of tactics may be needed, from an alteration of attitude on the part of the adolescent to a possible consideration of a change of school.

Rebellious attitudes should be dealt with by reasoned argument and not by a blanket imposition of rules. It is natural that teenagers should be concerned about many issues as they grow up and that parents should wish to avoid them making destructive and sometimes irreparable mistakes. However, it cannot be stressed too strongly that active co-operation between the two generations should begin in childhood and that parents should try both to set a good example and to agree together about upbringing.

IDEALISM

The belief by a young person that they are capable of changing the world and making it a better place is one of the most attractive features of adolescence and may be the forerunner to a lifetime's commitment. Parents should be careful not to dampen this enthusiasm by ridicule or statements such as 'you'll grow out of it', but, on the contrary, should be pleased that their teenager is developing a social conscience and concern. However, parents, and society as a whole, should be on their guard against those groups who seek to exploit youthful idealism for their own ends. Again, it is those parents who have retained their own standards, who take an active interest in the adolescent's ideas and aspirations, and who are able to talk to them freely, who are most likely to be effective against pernicious influences. All the evidence is that it is those teenage groups who feel disadvantaged and lacking a future in society who turn from idealism to violent and anti-social behaviour. Therefore it is very important for all teenagers to have a worthwhile goal and one which accords them a recognised and respected place in society.

GROUP BEHAVIOUR

Adolescents need to associate with and gain the approval of their peers. The groups with which they associate will depend very much upon their personality, social status, and education. Those teenagers who are socially and emotionally disadvantaged are more likely to become involved in criminal activities. It is important to stress here that social disadvantage does not necessarily imply living in a certain area or coming from a particular income group. As illustrated in films such as Lindsay Anderson's *If*, boys attending an exclusive public school can be equally as disadvantaged as those from poor backgrounds if they come from homes where there is no parental interest or affection. Moreover, the leaders of criminal youth gangs are often, like Graham Greene's Pinky in *Brighton Rock*, those teenagers whose innate intelligence has never been put to use by society and is thus diverted into criminality.

Parents are sometimes concerned that their adolescent is keeping 'bad company'. Sometimes, this is merely mixing with a group of friends of whom the parents do not approve for a variety of reasons. Such companionship may be a form of rebelling against what are perceived as strict parental standards and a desire to get to know a wider variety of people. Parents should avoid criticising the teenager's friends, since this only causes the teenager to defend them and to intensify the relationship. Parents should also be sure that their feelings are based upon a proper concern and are not merely irrational prejudices. They have to remember that their children are entitled to pick their own friends just as they are. Teenagers should be encouraged to bring their friends home in a non-critical and accepting atmosphere.

On other occasions, however, there is more general cause for concern if the adolescent is becoming involved in serious anti-social activity. The parents should endeavour to explore why this is happening and try to treat the cause. For example, shy, inarticulate youngsters who are not doing well at school may become involved in a rough gang because this is the only group which will accept them, using them as a kind of stooge. An adolescent, distressed by the parents' marital disharmony or over-high expectations for their achievements, may try to take revenge on them by joining a group of which the adolescent knows they will disapprove.

Parents, under these circumstances, should not only talk to the teenager about the dangers of such anti-social behaviour but, equally importantly, try to show that they understand the reasons for it. It is always best to adopt a positive attitude of trying to change a situation, rather than merely stressing the negative aspects of 'getting into trouble' and so on, since an unhappy adolescent may sometimes almost wish to bring disaster upon themselves to show how badly they are feeling. If there is a situation which seems insoluble, the parents should not be afraid to seek expert help. Under these circumstances, again, it is very important that the family should attend as a group with a shared problem. It is courting disaster to present the adolescent as the one whose behaviour has to be corrected, since this only reinforces negativistic and aggressive feelings which impair any relationship with the therapist.

Anti-social behaviour problems will be dealt with more fully in Chapter 8.

It must also be emphasised that most groups have more positive aspects than deleterious ones. They enable adolescents to make the tricky adjustment into adult life by learning how to socialise, hear others' points of view, discuss important issues, and engage in joint ventures. It also, hopefully, gives them the opportunity to realise that their parents are not as difficult, demanding, or old-fashioned as they thought. Allegiance to the peer group is very strong in adolescence and those who, for a variety of reasons, are not readily accepted may feel considerable distress. With increasing maturity, there should come sufficient belief in one's own judgement to stand out against the group if necessary. This desirable objective can be aided by encouraging the teenager to think for themselves and form their own judgement about a situation, rather than fostering blind conformity.

PARENTAL ATTITUDES

Parents cannot expect their children to behave responsibly if the example they set is one of irresponsibility. If they habitually drive recklessly without regard for other people, boast about how they have managed to gain advantage by cheating, or feel the solution to any problem is to indulge in aggressive behaviour, it cannot be a matter for surprise if their children copy them.

It often happens that parents disagree about upbringing, often for reasons which lie in their own childhood and adolescence. A parent who is very strict may fear that, if they relax, their teenager will form bad associations and get into trouble. They see good behaviour as having to be enforced by outside authority rather than as the result of self-discipline. Someone who tries to be extremely lenient may have had the earlier experience that the only way to cope with dominant parents was to constantly try to please. Thus they may feel they will only be loved if they accede to every adolescent whim, no matter how unwise they know it to be. Parents often try to relive their childhood through their children, sometimes to the extent of pushing them into occupations or activities for which the adolescent is obviously unsuited. An even more unhappy example is that of the parent who was treated aggressively in their formative years, and carried this pattern of behaviour on into the relationship with a marital partner and their children.

Adolescents use their parents as role models far more than is realised, with the possibility of both good and bad consequences.

If there is obvious disagreement between the parents, teenagers, like any other group, are prone to manipulate the situation. However, most of them do not feel happy about doing this, because it ultimately only increases their insecurity and uncertainty about how they should behave. Parents should try to agree between themselves about the guidelines of behaviour. If they cannot do so, it is much more appropriate for them to tell the adolescent about their differences, so that the subject can be discussed, rather than for parents to vie with each other to impose their own attitudes.

Naturally, there are no universal rules of behaviour that can be expounded, since what is considered to be desirable will depend on each individual case and upon the beliefs of the parents and teenagers themselves. However, one wise maxim is to avoid a pretence to beliefs which one does not really feel, since teenagers are quick to detect hypocrisy and to be critical of it. Moreover, one cannot necessarily expect one's children to share one's beliefs or ideals, no matter how strongly and sincerely they are held. Nor should parents feel afraid to confess to their teenagers that they have been anxious, frightened, or uncertain in some life situations. It is surprising how often worried teenage patients will question their therapist, once they have established a good rapport, about how the therapist has felt in similar circumstances. A wise therapist will try to give an honest answer, since teenagers seem to feel reassured if they can identify with and copy from an adult whom they respect.

Parents should not be discouraged, moreover, if the adolescent does not immediately accept any advice that they offer. They may be surprised to find that, after a few weeks, counsel that seemed to have been ignored is offered back as if the teenager had just thought of it for themselves.

Above all, parents should keep constantly in mind the pitfalls that lie in wait for the youngsters deprived of parental support. One only has to look around the large cities to see girls and boys of 14 or younger begging and sleeping rough. Parents should never let a relationship with an adolescent get to the stage when communication breaks down and the child leaves home for an unknown destination. No matter how difficult the behaviour, the parents should bear in mind that their teenager still needs them, despite all appearances to the contrary. If they find themselves in a position where they cannot cope, they should seek professional help, preferably before things come to a crisis point.

2

EMOTIONAL DEVELOPMENT AND PROBLEMS

Since adolescence is a period of rapid physiological and psychological change, it is to be expected that emotional problems are common at this time. Fortunately, most of them are transient and only become entrenched when they are not handled properly. It is a sad fact, however, that the provision of teenage services remains woefully inadequate, not least in the field of mental health. It can be difficult to find professionals who are experienced in handling teenage problems, despite the fact that it seems obvious that proper management at this time would reduce the incidence of psychological illness in later life. However, an increasing number of family doctors are becoming interested in adolescent problems, as are many voluntary agencies. (A list of these appears at the end of this book.) It is important that the teenager should be able to relate well to the person who is trying to help them, since it often takes some time before they can talk freely about their problems.

The most common problems are discussed here.

ANXIETIES

Anxieties occur in relation to many aspects of life. Anxiety can be defined as a feeling of fear that something unpleasant is about to happen. It is accompanied by physical changes that are designed to prepare the body for fight or flight, including dry mouth, increased heart and pulse rate, tensing of the muscles, and rapid breathing. Anxiety is a normal accompaniment to a transient stress situation such as an interview, examination, or competing in some event. Under these circumstances it is useful because it gives the individual an impetus to do better. However, if anxiety is uncontrolled it can become incapacitating, as witness the teenager who goes into an examination so nervous they cannot remember anything that they have learnt. Practice in preparation for events such as exams, competitions, auditions, and so on can help to cut down anxiety, as can relaxation techniques which can be done with the aid of a tape or at classes. Prolonged stress can be a potent cause of ill-health and so, if a teenager is prone to anxiety, it is important that they learn how to cope with it during these formative years.

The problem is that anxiety, because of its physical accompaniments, can become self-perpetuating so that the adolescent may become convinced that they have some serious illness. This is often particularly marked where there has been a serious illness in family or friends. Such anxieties, if they persist, require a physical examination by the family doctor and, very importantly, an *explanation* as to how anxiety symptoms arise. This type of problem needs to be taken seriously and acted upon promptly, since the longer the anxiety is allowed to persist, the more the idea of physical illness is reinforced. Moreover, although serious physical illness is fortunately rare these days in teenagers, its symptoms may mimic those of anxiety. Persistent complaints of a physical problem should always be investigated and medical advice obtained.

Transient anxieties are common in adolescents because they are being faced with new situations and because they have lost their childhood belief that their parents are infallible, all-powerful, and can be all-protective.

Among the most common fears are:

- feelings of being physically unattractive
- having no friends
- being rejected
- leaving home
- becoming ill
- finding communication difficult with parents
- worry about parental arguments
- worry about death of a parent
- failure in examinations
- looking a fool at an interview
- not getting a job or into university
- vague worries about whether life is worth living
- anxieties about sexual attitudes and behaviour
- death, which is suddenly seen as a permanent state, unlike

15

the early childhood attitude that dead people can get up and walk about again.

Anxiety about work, school, or emotional situations can be dealt with by an understanding discussion about the causes. Here, a fine line has to be drawn between parental expectations of success and putting undue pressure upon a child who cannot live up to those standards. Anxiety may also be reinforced by parental attitudes. The most extreme example must be the mother I heard in the waiting area of the infant welfare clinic saying to her toddler, 'If you don't behave yourself, I'll take you in to the doctor for an injection.' She was then surprised when the child screamed hysterically every time anyone in a white coat appeared. But more caring parents may also reinforce anxiety by overprotection. With the best intentions in the world they keep their children away from school and do everything for them, but succeed only in producing more anxiety.

Parents who are themselves anxious will pass this on to their children. A patient of mine, whose mother had acute anxiety at the prospect of even the smallest journey from home, had managed to conquer her fear of travelling, but still experienced vague anxiety symptoms such as frequency of micturition (desire to pass urine) whenever she travelled herself.

PHOBIAS

Phobias are fears attached to a specific object or situation. Fears about animals, spiders, and the dark are common in childhood and may be carried on into the teenage years. Other common phobias are those related to heights, crowded places, aeroplanes and flying, blushing in public and being stared at, going into a room where there is a crowd of people, and school phobia, which will be discussed in Chapter 6. Adolescents feel very unsure of themselves and their abilities, even if they disguise this insecurity with an air of bravado. Most phobias will disappear when they gain confidence and if those around are sympathetic. Anxieties and phobias should never be the subject of ridicule nor of practical jokes by siblings, since this only reinforces the fears. Instead, attention should be directed towards associating a fearful situation with a pleasant one. Thus, a fear of travelling may be alleviated if the teenager is going to meet friends for some enjoyable outing or a fear of animals by association with a particularly affectionate pet.

Fortunately, the drive towards health is strong in adolescence and anxieties and phobias usually disappear spontaneously. This process will be aided if the parents, while being sympathetic, do not collude with the fear and become overprotective. Nor should an attitude of invalidism or secondary gain from the phobia be encouraged. Thus, a teenager who becomes afraid of crowded places should not be allowed to stay at home and never travel or go into shops. This will only be the beginning of what can be life-long invalidism. On the contrary, attention should be directed to a gradual introduction to the thing that is feared – a short time in the train, bus, or crowded store, with reassurance and a positive goal, such as a new garment or special suit, for which to aim. Evidence shows that the sooner such a phobia is dealt with, the more quickly it disappears.

In a minority of teenagers, particularly those who have always been very shy, nervous, and anxious, fears may persist. Under these circumstances, treatment by a psychologist or psychotherapist will be very helpful. They will use counselling, relaxation, and various other techniques to alleviate potentially incapacitating conditions. Tranquillising drugs do not solve the problem for adolescents. They do not tackle the root cause of the problem and can be habit-forming.

Mention should be made of a condition which, hopefully, few adolescents will experience. This has been called the *post-traumatic stress disorder* and occurs in those who have been in a life-threatening and terrifying situation, as for example at the 1989 football disaster at Hillsborough. The adolescent may experience recurrent nightmares and be constantly preoccupied with what happened. There is frequently guilt that they have survived when their friends died and a feeling that they could, somehow, have done more to help them. Often, there is a feeling of numbness and unreality. The teenager may want to talk all the time about what happened, so that other interests are constricted. Alternatively, they may find it so painful that they cannot talk about it at all and adopt an attitude of complete denial. There are various other symptoms such as difficulty in sleeping, feelings of anxiety, sensitivity to noise and other stimuli, and fear of things which remind them of the situation.

It is not only publicised disasters which may produce this kind of response. An event such as a car accident or the death of a friend by drowning may produce a similar reaction. The survivors must be able to relive their experiences and come to terms with their guilt and fears under professional supervision. But this must also be associated with family support and understanding. Parents and siblings may be disconcerted to find that

17

survivors are so disturbed, since they may expect them to be overjoyed at being alive. However, to be suddenly confronted with a life-threatening situation is a very painful experience, and the anxiety and depression generated needs to be dissipated before the individual can resume a normal life. Self-help groups for survivors and contact with those who have experienced similar trauma are very helpful in this respect.

Anxiety may also manifest itself in physical ways such as *tics* or *stammering*. Tics are repetitive movements, particularly of the facial muscles. Stammering involves difficulty in pronouncing consonants such as 'b', 'g', 's', or 't'. Both are worse in times of stress such as examinations, interviews, or public appearances. They are often reinforced by ridicule or imitation by other people and parents should stress to relatives and siblings that they should on no account do this.

Stammering, in particular, is worsened by the efforts the stammerer makes to avoid words with which they have difficulty. Parents can help by encouraging a relaxed attitude and, in the case of stammering, helping the teenager to concentrate on the words with which they have a problem and to practise saying them, aloud and repetitively, at home so that they can gain confidence. It also sometimes helps to start a sentence with a word which it is less difficult to pronounce. For example, when approaching a rail ticket office the teenager, instead of saying 'Birmingham, please' could say 'Can I have a ticket to Birmingham, please'.

Again, expert advice and help is available for those cases in which the problem does not respond to simple measures.

OBSESSIONS

Obsessions are ideas, images, impulses, or patterns of behaviour in which a subjective sense of compulsion is opposed by a conscious and deliberate resistance. Obsessions are repetitive, unpleasant, unwelcome, and accompanied by emotional tension. A typical example would be the development of a feeling that everything one touches is contaminated by germs, so that the hands have to be continually washed. No matter how hard the individual tries to avoid the hand washing, anxiety builds up and is only relieved when the hands are washed. Almost immediately the whole cycle starts again, so that severely obsessional individuals will be washing their hands, and often everything they touch, many, many times during the day. As can be imagined, this is both disabling and distressing.

Minor forms of obsessional behaviour are seen in the super-stitious acts of children and adolescents, particularly in times of tension. A student may have to prepare his notes in a set way, take certain pens or mascots to an examination, or look out for various indications that they will have good luck, such as buses coming in a certain order or traffic lights remaining green while they pass.

There is a particular type of personality which has been called the obsessional personality. Such individuals are extremely conscientious with very high standards of right or wrong and extremely critical, both of themselves and others, if they fall below those standards. One view is that such individuals can develop anxiety as a result of a conflict between their high moral standards and some desire that they have which seems unworthy of them. Such conflicts, particularly of a sexual nature, may be marked in adolescence and affect such a personality more than it would an easy-going one. Teenagers with an obsessional type of personality should be encouraged to take a more relaxed view of life and not to be hypercritical. Clearly there must be a balance about this, because a certain measure of obsessional traits – such as meticulousness, conscien-tiousness, and application to work – are obviously necessary in any sphere. They only become incapacitating if carried to extremes.

Occasionally at this time, serious obsessions may develop and become disabling. There may be persistent and distressing thoughts about aggressive acts or sexual situations, which the sufferer *fears* they may carry out. It should be stressed that these are anxieties and not something that will be carried out in practice. The adolescent, however, may constantly need to be reassured that they are not going to commit some anti-social act. There may be compulsions to check everything, to wash constantly, or to count things in the house endlessly. Unless it is appreciated that this condition of obsessional neurosis is an illness, it can appear aggravating and bizarre. Parents who feel that their teenager is becoming incapacitated by obsessional preoccupations and habits should not hesitate to seek medical advice since, as with anxiety, the sooner treatment begins the better. A great deal can be done to help such conditions and alleviate the distress they cause. Many obsessionals try to hide their symptoms because they are ashamed of their strange nature and fear people will think they are going mad. This is not the case and teenagers can be reassured of this and should be encouraged to seek help.

DEPRESSION

Depression in relation to life events is common in adolescence, as indeed it is at all ages. An unhappy love affair, an examination failure, rejection for a job, a quarrel with a schoolfriend, or home problems will produce a feeling of lowness of spirits and sadness. It may also occur after a physical illness, particularly a viral one such as influenza or glandular fever. Fortunately, in most cases the mood quickly passes. Characteristically, the teenager is less depressed when something pleasant happens or they are with their friends, and the condition improves rapidly when the long-term situation changes, for example if they acquire a new boyfriend or girlfriend. Parents can obviously help by being sympathetic and understanding and also offering practical advice, especially with regard to examinations or job interviews.

They should be concerned, however, if the gloomy mood appears to be deepening, since these symptoms may be the start of a depressive illness which will require psychiatric treatment. Such depression tends to worsen if the teenager is in a situation which is extremely emotionally damaging to them. The examination failure may be the last straw in a series of setbacks or the unhappy love affair the culmination of a number of rejections. Depression is less likely to get better if the adolescent is already socially isolated, has few friends, and feels they have no support at home. Under these circumstances, there may be an impulsive suicide attempt which, unfortunately, may end in physical damage or even death. Serious difficulty in sleeping, loss of appetite and interest in things, sad or indifferent mood which does not lift in response to pleasant life events, and talk of unworthiness and suicide must always be taken very seriously indeed and immediate medical help sought. At such times it may be necessary for the teenager to see a professional skilled in counselling, for family therapy to take place, or even for the teenager to be given a short course of treatment with anti-depressant drugs which are not habit-forming and which alleviate depression.

ANXIETY OVER THE BODY IMAGE

This is common in adolescence, since teenagers naturally wish to appear as attractive as possible. Parents can help by encouraging a healthy diet, exercise, proper skin care to avoid spots, an attractive hairstyle, and so on. Adolescents need reassurance that they are attractive, but this has to be given in subtle ways so that they do not feel they are being patronised. It is also important to make the teenager feel that the parents value them as a person and that they have valuable qualities which others will find attractive.

SHYNESS

Adolescents often feel gauche, uncertain of themselves, fearful of making some social blunder, looking a fool, or being laughed at by others. This is particularly so in the presence of those they wish to impress and there may be overcompensation in the form of showing off and loud behaviour. Girls tend to giggle, whilst boys are more inclined to become noisy and boastful. This is a stage which settles down when social skills become more accomplished and, normally, needs little parental intervention. Some teenagers, however, are crippled by shyness and in such cases it is important that self-esteem is boosted as much as possible. Such adolescents should be gently encouraged to join in social activities and reminded that others often feel just as shy as they do. They should not be forced into large gatherings and made to socialise, since their inevitable embarrassment will pave the way for rejection and reinforcement of their shyness. It is probably best if they form a few close friendships rather than trying to be too gregarious. In early adolescence, in particular, it is a rare boy or girl who is able to be caring enough to help someone else who is very shy. Therefore, it is important that the adolescents themselves make an effort to overcome their social awkwardness, particularly with a small group of people with whom they have something in common. It is also important to bear in mind the personality of the teenager. Some people are naturally outgoing, and find it easy to make friends and to become the life and soul of the party. Others are more solitary, enjoy quiet occupations, and are more contented with their own company. Parents should accept this and not try to force one personality to become another.

WORRIES OVER PARENTAL RELATIONSHIPS

Adolescents need to respect and love both parents and it is extremely distressing for them to be involved in quarrels, infidelities, or violence. In a sensitive teenager it can lead to difficulties in their own adjustment or to serious emotional disturbance. Because of the difficulties of self-expression at this time, and particularly in early adolescence, they may take refuge in withdrawn, truculent behaviour, complaints of illness, or anti-social activities.

Parents should not try to involve teenagers in their disputes, asking them to take sides, no matter how tempting this may be. Children and adolescents are able to accept that their parents can have an argument or disagree, in the way that they do with their friends. It becomes distressing only when unpleasant insinuations are made or when there are threats. If there is a real cause for serious disagreement, this should be discussed with the adolescent by both parents, without either blaming the other. The teenager has to be brought to see that there are situations in life where people cannot get along or must agree to differ. If the parents intend to separate, they should make it clear why this is happening and, very importantly, they should emphasise that it is not the child's fault and that both parents still love them. A parent should never just vanish without giving an explanation, although superficially it may seem that this is the least painful thing to do. Such a disappearance will only make the teenager feel bitter that the parent did not seem to care enough to say goodbye to them.

Parental separation is always very upsetting for an adolescent. In some cases where there has been prolonged disharmony, it may come as a relief, but there is always a feeling of sadness that the parents cannot stay together. Acceptance of the fact that such separation is sometimes inevitable is a part of growing up, but can still be painful. Parents need to be particularly understanding at such times, often under circumstances where they themselves are undergoing considerable emotional upheaval. The most essential thing is that they should continue to maintain their individual relationship with their child and enable them to see the other partner as a worthwhile person. Even if one parent feels they have been wronged, they should, for the sake of their child, try to stress the positive aspects of their marriage.

STEPFAMILIES

These days many teenagers acquire step-parents and step-siblings. Such families may encounter a number of problems. There are divided loyalties towards the biological parents, sometimes made worse by the circumstances of the separation. The teenager often feels displaced from the affections of both parents by rivals. There is a refusal to accept that the step-parent has a disciplinary role and a distaste for open affection or sexuality between the parent and step-parent. This is often compounded by the fact that the step-parent is jealous and resentful of what can sometimes be a disagreeable teenager. The latter's attitude may veer disconcertingly from a demand for instant love from the new step-parent, to a refusal to have anything to do with them. The teenager may reject the new arrangement precisely because it signifies the death of their previous two-parent family and abolishes the fantasy that it can be re-created. Moreover, there are jealousies and rivalries between the step-siblings. Things are not helped if the natural parents are fostering a feeling of discontent for their own ends.

Becoming a step-parent requires a special type of tolerance, to the extent that an organisation of self-help groups, the National Stepfamily Association, has been formed to help with the problems that may occur when remarriage results in new family members. There are a number of cardinal rules to bear in mind in this situation. Before remarrying, each adult involved has to realise that they must be able to accept and come to an understanding with their step-children. They have to remember that adolescents go through a difficult time even under normal circumstances and that the breakdown of their parents' marriage exacerbates these problems and insecurities. They should seriously consider whether they can assume responsibility for their step-children in the sense of being fair to them, giving them the affection and the support that they give to their own children. The step-parents should resolve that they will not give preference or greater tolerance to their own biological children, no matter how tempting it may sometimes be to do so. Nor should they compare one child to the disadvantage of the other. They should remember that it is not the teenager's fault that the previous marriage ended and that the harm done to an adolescent who feels rejected or unfairly treated by parents can be incalculable. On the other hand, just like the biological parents, they should not allow a manipulative teenager to cause a rift between them. It has to be realised that building a relationship requires time and patience, but that a caring step-parent can form bonds of friendship with a step-child that can be mutually rewarding and supportive.

THE SINGLE PARENT

Many parents, the majority of them women, find themselves

alone looking after one or more children, usually as a result of divorce, but sometimes following death.

The problems under these two circumstances are probably rather different. The death of a parent is a frightening experience for a teenager and they may find it hard to express grief to the remaining parent for fear of upsetting them more. The general taboo about death in our society does not help. The school class of one teenager were all instructed by the teacher never to mention his dead mother in case it upset him, so that he felt that no one cared that she had died and that she had been completely forgotten. What he wanted to do was to talk about her and work through his grief. It is important that the surviving parent, siblings, relatives, and friends should talk about the deceased parent, recalling happy times together and keeping their memory alive. If the parent does not speak about their partner, the teenager may assume that they have been too speedily forgotten. As in many bereavements, the dead parent may initially be idealised so that any faults or disagreements are forgotten and the remaining parent may be blamed for excessive strictness. This will disappear as the adolescent comes to terms with the loss.

Where separation has been due to a divorce, there may be additional problems associated with the absent parent's attitudes. Single-parent families are often financially poor and there may be jealousies associated with a stepfamily, particularly if the new partner does not accept the teenager. The single parent, often hurt and resentful, may use the adolescent as a confidante to complain about their ex-partner's feelings, increasing the adolescent's conflict about the parental separation. There may be attempts at bribery, emotional or financial, by either partner anxious to retain their child's affection or to assuage their own guilt. If the single parent and adolescent are of opposite sexes, there can be discipline problems and difficulties in discussing sexual matters.

A single parent has to guard against making the adolescent excessively dependent or trying to put them in the role of the absent partner. They should try to ensure that the teenager develops their own friends and interests and be prepared to accept that they will leave home and make a life for themselves. They can help this process by developing new friends and becoming involved in work and hobbies themselves, so that their children do not feel guilty about them. They should endeavour to form the basis of an adult relationship with the teenager, by talking to them openly and allowing the adolescent to do the same. Nor should they allow teenage jealousies to interfere with them forming new friendships. The teenager has to realise that their parent needs fulfillment in life just as they do and, provided such new relationships are handled considerately and sensitively, the adolescent can only benefit. Understanding friends and relations and self-help groups such as Cruse (for widows and widowers) and Gingerbread (for one-parent families) may be invaluable. Grandparents may also be of great help, particularly if, as often happens, the teenager feels they can talk to them freely. Every effort should be made to maintain contact with both sets of grandparents, since a teenager will already have established a relationship with them. The fact that a marriage has ended should not be the signal for whole families to take sides to the extent that a vulnerable adolescent becomes ostracised.

ADOPTIVE PARENTS

Children should always be told that they are adopted as soon as they are able to understand the idea. This fact should never be left until the teenage years, as it sometimes used to be, because this is the time when children are least able to cope with such a revelation. They are already searching for their identity and the discovery that they have biological parents about whom they know nothing comes as a considerable and often long-lasting shock. Adoptive parents may, understandably, feel hurt that, during the teenage years, there is often a drive to discover and know more about their natural parents. However, this is not unnatural since teenagers frequently feel they need to know more about their roots and the reasons why they were given up for adoption. The adolescent may or may not be successful in their quest, but the adoptive parents should not feel that they have been rejected. Rather, they should regard it as a tribute to the fact that they have brought up the teenager to have an understanding nature which will enable them to continue a close relationship with them into adult life. They should also be aware that the adolescent may sometimes experience a painful rejection from natural parents who see them as threatening a present relationship, and be prepared to offer understanding and support.

3

LEARNING DIFFICULTIES

Parents are often concerned because their children are not making the academic progress for which they had hoped.

There can be a variety of reasons for this.

PARENTS' OVEREXPECTATIONS

The teenager may, in fact, be making adequate progress for their intellectual level. Intelligence has been viewed by some psychologists as a general capacity for comprehension and reasoning, whilst others have regarded it as being made up of a number of mental abilities which are relatively independent of each other. The well-known psychologist Thurstone, for example, identified seven factors as the primary mental abilities, all of which can be assessed by intelligence tests:

- verbal comprehension: the ability to understand the meaning of words as measured by vocabulary tests
- word fluency: the ability to think of words rapidly, such as matching words which mean the same or ones that rhyme with others
- number: the ability to work with numbers and perform calculations
- space: the ability to visualise space–form relationships, as in recognising the same figures presented in a different orientation
- memory: the ability to recall verbal stimuli such as word pairs or sentences
- perceptual speed: the ability to grasp visual details quickly and to see similarities and differences between pictured objects
- reasoning: the ability to find a general rule on the basis of

presented instances. A simple example would be working out what numbers follow in a given sequence such as 2 3 5 8 ...

There is controversy as to how far intelligence is inherited, although there is certainly a fairly considerable genetic element. A person's genes can be regarded as imposing a top and bottom limit on intelligence with a possible range of intellectual ability between those limits. It is clear that an individual can be helped to achieve the maximum potential of their intellectual ability by a stimulating home environment, good physical and mental health, and skilled educational methods. However, there are limits and it would be foolish, for example, for parents to set their heart upon their child becoming a doctor when, already at the age of 13, they continue, despite good teaching, to struggle with even the basic concepts of science. It would be much wiser to concentrate upon the subjects which come more easily to the adolescent and plan a career around those. Parents should also accept the special talents a teenager may have in areas such as art and music, rather than trying to force them into what the parents might see as more conventional fields of study.

Where there is serious concern about academic progress, it would be helpful to obtain an assessment of general intellectual ability from an educational psychologist. This will give an overall profile of the child's strengths and weaknesses and show whether, for instance, they have some special difficulties with arithmetical problems or space–form relationships. It should be emphasised that such tests act only as a general guide and can be affected by a number of factors, not least of which are anxiety and the skill and patience of the tester. Such assessment would comprise a wide range of questions – the meaning of words, arithmetic problems, completing and arranging pictures and object assembly, and memory and attention as tested by digit span, in which a series of numbers spoken by the tester have to be repeated forwards or backwards. General reasoning and comprehension is tested by asking questions such as 'why it is important to be able to read?' or 'why is it necessary to have laws?'

PHYSICAL HEALTH

No one can learn adequately when they are feeling ill and any prolonged or chronic illness can interfere with an adolescent's school progress. Often these are conditions which can be easily remedied, such as anaemia resulting from a faulty diet or excessive menstrual blood loss. Where there is prolonged lethargy and an absence of the interest and spontaneity which is usually characteristic of adolescence, the possibility of physical illness must not be excluded.

PSYCHOLOGICAL FACTORS

A teenager who is worried or depressed has, naturally, little interest in learning. Their mind is constantly straying to their problem, so that they do not concentrate on their studies and have difficulty in remembering what they are being taught. Sometimes the reason for their concern will be obvious, if there is some serious home difficulty. Such a situation should be remedied if at all possible. Quarrelling parents, for instance, should realise how they are affecting their child and try to resolve their differences. It may be, however, that there is a situation, such as the serious illness of a parent or a sibling, which causes prolonged anxiety. Under these circumstances the parents should talk to the adolescent and enable them to give vent to their fears. It is sometimes the case that a teenager has misinterpreted an event and believes, for instance, that their father is seriously ill with a cancer, when in reality he is only entering hospital for a straightforward operation.

The problem may lie, not within the home, but at school. There may be bullying and a clever child may pretend to be a dunce in order to fit in with their peers. On the other hand, a not so clever teenager who is struggling to keep up with more academically brilliant boys or girls may give up completely and not make the most of their potential. Parents should expect their child to do as well as they possibly can and praise their achievements, but they should not make comparisons, either in their own minds or especially to the teenager, with others who are doing better academically. They should regard their child as an individual who has their own positive qualities. They should also appreciate that intellectual brilliance is by no means the sole or even the most important criterion in making a success of one's life. Even academically, it is often those who are persistent and prepared to work hard who finally have the best attainments. Moreover, academic progress is rarely uniform and a teenager who seems uninterested may take off when they develop an interest in a certain topic or are stimulated by a good teacher.

The adolescent may be failing because of faulty teaching

28

methods or because they are fearful of or dislike a particular teacher. A shy, diffident teenager may well feel timid of asking a macho or sarcastic teacher about any difficulties they have in the teacher's subject. It sometimes happens, in a subject such as maths and particularly in large classes, that the individual misses out on some vital step and then cannot catch up. If this happens because of illness, the parent can obtain the school work so that the adolescent can study it when they are feeling better. Parents should not hesitate to talk to the teachers about their child's progress and, naturally, they will achieve better results if they approach them in a friendly way, enlisting their co-operation and seeking their advice rather than being critical. They should make it clear that they expect to do their share in helping the child and would appreciate constructive suggestions, unlike the explanation given to a learned colleague of mine with a vast and comprehensive library. He was upset to be told, when questioning his son's poor results in English, that this was because he obviously did not have a single book in the house and the boy lacked stimulation. Incidentally, the boy obtained an excellent university degree in English, after a change of school. On the other hand, one cannot overestimate the influence that a good teacher can have in adolescence, particularly for those children who, for whatever reason, feel insecure or inferior to others or who have felt previously that learning is not for them.

Overanxiety about performance will also adversely affect attainments. If an adolescent knows, when they bring their school report home, that they will be subjected to a barrage of adverse criticism and derogatory comparison with others, it is not likely to stimulate their interest in school work. Severe anxiety, in itself, militates against learning. Parental indifference to any achievement is just as bad, particularly for a clever child. Parents should aim for a realistic appraisal of their teenager's ability and encourage an attitude that study and learning should be approached in a relaxed way and be enjoyable. They should never make the child feel that school is a kind of punishment or designed to get them out of the way or that studying is a waste of time.

HABITS OF STUDY

It goes without saying that a teenager should have a quiet, comfortable place in which to study. They should not be expected to study with the television blaring or when the whole family is talking. However, a number of them do appear to be able to concentrate whilst listening to music of varying degrees of loudness.

Concentration and memory are impaired by fatigue, so studying and homework should be done preferably in the early evening before the adolescent becomes too tired. Whilst they should be expected to do their share of household chores, it is important that school work should be done first and that, particularly prior to examinations, they are given ample time for revision. Parents should take an active interest in the subjects that the teenager is studying and try to help if there are difficulties. Help does not mean that the parent should do the project for the adolescent, but that they should perhaps suggest a possible new approach to the subject matter or books that could usefully be read. They should also be willing to read essays, if requested, and try to make constructive comments. This does not mean that parents need know all about every subject that the teenager is studying. One of the important factors in essay writing, for example, is that the writer should be able to develop ideas and make them easily understood by someone who knows little of the subject.

Academic achievement can obviously be impaired by faulty study habits. If one is learning facts in a subject, the material has first to be read and understood. The important facts have then to be committed to memory, the first task being to distinguish those facts from unimportant ones. Memory is improved by repetition and constant re-examination of facts stored in it. Essential facts should be gone over at frequent intervals by writing them out, repeating them aloud, or rehearsing them in the mind. It is not sufficient to constantly read the same things over again. There has to be a positive effort to memorise them and to put them into an orderly sequence within the mind, preferably in relation to facts that are there already. For example, when studying a particular country's geography, the facts about it have to be associated with what one knows about the history, any film that one saw about it, songs and music that one has heard, or television documentaries about its environment and wildlife. Such an association is a valuable aid to memory.

If a teenager is weak in one particular subject and requires it in order to qualify for a career, it is worth considering having them coached, arranging extra work, or trying to go over the material with them on a one-to-one basis. This often overcomes the anxiety that may be felt in a large class when the individual is too diffident to ask about points that they have not understood. Moreover, if there are features about a certain subject that the adolescent cannot grasp, they may well develop a block about it, finding it increasingly difficult to cope with it at all.

EXAMINATIONS

Most adolescents have to face examinations of varying degrees of difficulty during the teenage years, but, if adequately prepared, they need not view these with undue anxiety.

Examinations are often made less fearful if the adolescent becomes accustomed to regular testing in familiar surroundings – a weekly vocabulary test or having to write an essay in class in a set time. Parents can also help by testing the teenager on learned material, if they request it. Such requests are more likely to be made if they feel the parents are interested and will be patient with any mistakes they make.

There are a number of things that can be useful in coping with examinations.

- Stress the positive aspects and try to make the teenager feel that an examination is a goal to be achieved rather than an ordeal to be endured.
- Try to obtain some understanding of the examination system so that you can understand what it is that is required for a given further course of study.
- Try to evaluate the merits of different universities and polytechnics in relation to what your child wishes to study. Prospective students are usually invited to see these for themselves and careers officers at school will provide guidance.
- Examination preparation requires a system of study over a period of time. It is completely counter-productive for anyone to try to learn things for an examination the night before. Anxiety will prevent any new learning and trying to digest a mass of facts will only produce confusion. All learning should be completed at least a couple of days before the examination and the ensuing time devoted to thinking about possible questions and framing answers to them – and to relaxation.
- Many students in examinations lose marks because they do not answer the question which is being asked. They have revised a certain topic such as 'Oliver Cromwell's Irish policy' or 'the way in which the body deals with proteins'. They then try to regurgitate what they have learnt in answer

31

to a question such as 'Was Cromwell's attitude to Ireland a reflection of his Puritanism?' or 'Discuss the role of the kidney in body metabolism', questions which are asking something rather different and are expecting the candidate to critically evaluate their knowledge.

When sitting an examination, candidates should read all the paper through and spend a little time underlining the key words in the questions they have decided to answer. A question which asks, 'Does Dickens present a realistic view of childhood in his novels?' has rather different implications to, 'Is Dickens the first novelist to see children as individuals in his novels?', although both will obviously include some of the same material.

- Students should be sure that they divide their time in the examination sensibly. They should remember that, no matter how well they do a question, the maximum mark they can obtain is only a percentage of the total mark. Therefore, if one is answering four questions, it is much better to get 15 out of 25 marks on each, rather than 20 marks on two and only 5 marks on the other two, because time has not been allowed to answer them adequately. Students should spend an equal time on each question, bearing in mind that the majority of marks are gained in the early part of the answer.

- Examination failure should never be regarded as the end of the world. In most cases exams can be repeated, so that better grades are attained. It is important that the reasons for failure should be evaluated in the expectation of success next time. One thing that must be avoided is building up the idea that a teenager can never pass examinations. It is important that any retake is done after adequate preparation and when the candidate feels confident that they can do better.

4

EATING PROBLEMS

To many parents it may seem a contradiction to talk about a healthy diet in relation to teenagers, who are popularly supposed to stuff themselves with chips, hamburgers, ice-cream, chocolate, fizzy sugary drinks, and so on. However, the majority of adolescents are becoming increasingly health-conscious, preoccupied with their weight and physical appearance. Therefore it is often not too difficult to encourage them into healthier eating, particularly if the foods offered are made appetising. After all, a lettuce, normally only attractive to a rabbit in its plain form, can be rendered quite delicious with the addition of a tasty low-fat dressing.

CONSTITUENTS OF A HEALTHY DIET

Ideally this should be HIGH IN FIBRE and LOW IN FAT.

Fibre is desirable because it helps combat bowel problems and is particularly effective in preventing constipation. It is found in wholegrain products such as cereals, in fruit and vegetables and in beans, including those old favourites, baked beans. So a snack of baked beans on wholemeal toast could not be better. Fresh fruit and vegetables should be eaten raw as often as possible since heating destroys some of the nutrients.

Animal fat is high in calories and so contributes to obesity; it is associated with health problems and heart disease in later life. Excessive fat consumption is considered a contributory factor in acne and other skin disorders. All visible fat should preferably be cut off from meat and there should be a limited intake of foods containing animal fat, such as cream and butter. Food should always be grilled, which removes a considerable part of the fat content.

Protein for tissue building is an essential part of the diet and is

33

found in meat, fish, poultry, eggs, cheese, pulses, and grains.

Carbohydrates are necessary for energy and this is probably why sugary snacks are so popular. However, these foods often have very little other nutritional value and tend to give a quick burst of vitality followed by a slump. Wholegrain foods, fruit and vegetables are much better sources of carbohydrates.

Everyone must take a certain amount of **vitamins** to keep alive and in good health, which is why the word comes from 'vita', the Latin word for 'life'. Small quantities are enough for the body's needs and, for someone on a varied diet, there should be no need for vitamin supplements. Indeed, excessive amounts of vitamins, particularly vitamins A and D which are stored in the body because they are fat-soluble, can be harmful.

Vitamin A helps to prevent infection and night blindness and is important in the health of skin, teeth, and bones. It is found in eggs, cheese, milk, apricots, water melon, liver, beetroot, broccoli, carrots, and spinach.

Vitamin B is actually a group of vitamins which have important functions in relation to concentration, memory, mood, nerve conduction, and general body metabolism. They are found in milk, fresh fruit and vegetables, and cereals. They are not retained in the body and, therefore, must be regularly replaced in the diet.

Vitamin C is essential for the proper maintenance of the bones, joints, and gums, and as a buffer against infection. It is found in citrus fruit like oranges and lemons, in strawberries, blackcurrants, mangoes, tomatoes, and green vegetables. It is readily destroyed by heat, which is why vegetables should not be overcooked and should be eaten raw if possible. Like the vitamin B group, vitamin C is not stored in the body and must be taken regularly.

Vitamin D is needed for bone formation and sound teeth. Its effect is helped by sunlight. It is found in oily fish like mackerel, salmon, and herring, and in dairy products such as milk, eggs, butter, cheese, margarine, and liver.

Minerals such as calcium, iron, magnesium, and zinc are also essential constituents of a healthy diet.

Iron, a very important mineral, is required for the formation of haemoglobin in red blood cells and occurs in meat, fish, chicken, egg yolks, wholegrain bread, shellfish, green vegetables, raisins, prunes, and apricots.

Calcium, vital for healthy bone growth, occurs in dairy products and, when necessary, as in a slimming diet, it can be supplied in semi-skimmed or skimmed milk where the fat content is decreased.

There are several basic rules in designing a diet for teenagers. Obviously they should eat the same meals as the rest of the family. They should not be the recipient of special delicacies, the supreme example of which must be the doting mother who gave her son fillet steak and the rest of the family scrag end of a very inedible type. When they leave home, no one else is going to give them that kind of misguided treatment. Nor should food fads for their own sake be encouraged since, again, an excessively delicate appetite is not a preparation for adult life, particularly if one has to dine in a works canteen or a university hall of residence.

However, consideration should be given to individual likes and dislikes. A number of adolescents feel repulsed at the idea of eating animals and they should not be pressurised to do so. The general consensus of opinion is that we would all do better to eat less red meat, substituting fish, if acceptable, cheese, egg, and vegetable dishes. Others cannot bear fat and cut off every scrap, others dislike eggs that are runny, or some other particular type of food. Meals should be of reasonable size, but not overlarge, since the consumption of vast quantities becomes a habit that can lead to obesity, and they should be tastefully flavoured with sauces and dressings. Moreover, whilst it is desirable to cultivate a healthy diet, this should not become a fetish where certain foods, often beloved of teenagers and many others for that matter, such as bacon sandwiches or fish and chips, are never allowed in the house. It is also wise to avoid too much talk of certain foods being 'good for you' in front of adolescents. The effect of this on some of them in certain moods is that they immediately decide that they will reject them. Again, it should be emphasised that healthy eating begins from early childhood. This does not mean that parents, as they sometimes do, must ban all sweets, chocolate, crisps, and so on. Children have to mix with others who eat these things, and human and especially adolescent nature being what it is, forbidden things become more desirable. It is just wise to set limits upon their consumption by offering healthy alternatives.

SENSIBLE WEIGHT REDUCTION

Obesity frequently begins in childhood or adolescence. It is a health hazard and, particularly in a society which is geared to the concept that slim is beautiful, a cause of powerful psychological problems, as can be seen by reading any slimming magazine. It can be prevented in the majority of cases by a sensible diet and regular exercise. There may sometimes be a rapid weight gain in early adolescence which settles down in a couple of years.

Before embarking upon dieting to reduce weight in a teenager, consideration has to be given to whether the adolescent is really overweight, which can be done by reference to height and weight tables. An excessive drive for unreasonable thinness may be a precursor of anorexia nervosa, which will be discussed later in the chapter. Psychological factors, particularly eating for comfort and to alleviate unhappiness, play an important part in producing and maintaining obesity and, unless these are dealt with, the teenager may become involved in a life-long battle of dieting–weight gain–dieting which is never resolved. Such individuals should never be ridiculed about their weight in the mistaken belief that they enjoy the joke as much as anyone else, although it is difficult to see why being overweight is considered so funny. Often the result is that they console themselves with yet another calorie-laden meal. It has to be remembered that dieting is very difficult and that hunger can be a powerful spur to breaking a diet. Therefore it is essential for the teenager to be occupied and to be involved in activities, particularly those which require physical exertion such as walking, swimming, cycling, football, or tennis.

There are a variety of diets which can be used to reduce weight and the adolescent can choose the one they prefer, varying them from time to time. There are several points to be borne in mind.

- Very low-calorie diets are not to be recommended for teenagers, since their growth spurt requires them to have a wide range of adequate nutrients. Moreover, such diets do not teach the healthy eating habits which are essential for permanent weight maintenance and they may also be followed by a rapid weight increase when stopped.

  Not less than 1200 calories should be taken with the addition of one multivitamin/mineral supplement daily. Details of many varieties of such diets are to be found in countless magazines and books and, since variety is essential, no single one is reproduced here. Calorie contents of most foods are easily obtainable and will aid in designing a personal diet to suit individual requirements.

- Slimming tablets should *not* be used. They are habit-forming and, again, do not encourage the knowledge about nutrition essential to maintain a reasonable weight.

- The diet should be practised along with a good amount of

exercise. Although moderate exercise in itself does not lead to a great weight loss, it is invaluable for strengthening muscle tone.

- Many calories can be saved by simple measures which do not interfere with the taste of food. Food should be grilled not fried, low-calorie dressing used, portions should be weighed and not guessed at, low-fat products such as certain cheeses can be eaten, semi-skimmed milk can be used and products low in sugar substituted for high-sugar ones. For example, two large pork sausages fried contain about 100 more calories than similar ones which are grilled. Low-fat spread can be used instead of butter and slimmer's bread instead of ordinary.

- Use should be made of relatively low-calorie food such as fruit and vegetables.

- One of the reasons for diet failure is monotony. Therefore menus should be varied rather than sticking with the cold meat and salad recipes.

- Try to include the whole family in the diet. Nothing is more discouraging than for a teenager to be picking at a few lettuce leaves whilst the rest of the family is enjoying spaghetti bolognese. The latter can be made to a slimmer's recipe and the person on the diet can have a smaller portion.

- A positive attitude towards losing weight should be encouraged, stressing the advantages of feeling fitter, being able to buy nice clothes, and so on. However, parents have to be careful not to go to the opposite extreme and behave as if attaining an ideal weight was the only thing that mattered in life. Nor should the teenager be made to feel they have committed some heinous crime if they occasionally tuck into a Mars bar. Most important of all, they should *not* be teased about their weight.

- A diet should be seen as a step along the way to a lifetime's healthy eating, not as a penance. Snack eating and overindulgence is frequently a sign of boredom, so the teenager should keep busy and be as active as possible.

- A weight loss of 1–2 lbs per week should be aimed at. It is better to lose weight gradually; excessive expectations of rapid weight loss can lead to discouragement and premature abandonment of the diet.

- Try to pick a time when the adolescent is not under too much pressure, such as school holidays, to commence the diet. If there is another overweight family member, it can be encouraging if they both commence dieting at the same time.

- Slimming should never be allowed to become an end in itself. Once a normal weight has been gained, an eating regime should be instituted which keeps the weight at this level.

EATING DISORDERS

Fortunately most teenagers have healthy appetites, even if their parents are sometimes not happy with what they eat. However, there are two serious eating disorders which can occur at this time of which parents, who are often best-placed to observe eating behaviour, should be aware.

Anorexia nervosa

This is a condition which has received wide publicity and has been misnamed 'the slimmer's disease'. Normal weight loss on a healthy restricted calorie diet has nothing in common with this illness, which can be potentially life-threatening.

It is predominantly found in young females (over 90 per cent of sufferers are girls) and is characterised by a drastic reduction in food intake in the erroneous belief that the adolescent is too fat. Initially, only foods that are regarded as very low in calories will be taken and the starvation may become so severe that a sufferer may be eating only one slice of ham or a small portion of lettuce and tomatoes per day. If the family insists that food is eaten, it may secretly be vomited back or hidden. A mother of a patient of mine found that every hiding place in her daughter's bedroom had been filled with food that had been given to her as, for example, sandwiches for school lunches. The starvation induces cessation of the menstrual periods (amenorrhoea) and the weight loss can be extremely drastic, with weight dropping to between 5 and 6 stone (30–35 kilos). After the early stages, there is usually little hunger and sufferers are often characterised by considerable bursts of activity.

One of the most interesting features of anorexia nervosa is the individual's altered perception of their body image. A girl who was a shapely beauty queen and now looks like a famine skeleton, when shown pictures of herself then and now, will unhesitatingly say that she looks better now because she is 'nice and slim'. It cannot be emphasised too strongly that this is a serious illness which, untreated, can end fatally. The lack of adequate nutrition can predispose to overwhelming infection or grave disturbances of the bodily organs and metabolism.

Hopefully, the wider recognition of this condition will lead to earlier diagnosis and treatment before full anorexia becomes established. In severe cases the individual cannot be relied upon to eat even if they promise to do so, and supervision in a hospital setting may be required. Treatment is directed towards progression back to a normal weight, but most importantly of all, therapy aims to help the patient understand the problems which have resulted in this condition. Sometimes anorexia nervosa results when a slimming diet is carried too far, particularly where there has been teasing about obesity. However, many anorexics are of a reasonably normal weight when the illness begins, although they are always preoccupied with bodily shape.

There have been a number of theories put forward as to why psychological problems are manifested in this particular way. Certainly anorexia can occur when a family has been disrupted by divorce or when the child is experiencing sexual problems. The fact that such adolescents tend to regress to a rather dependent state, that they wish to reduce their body to a state in which all secondary sexual characteristics disappear and there is a loss of menstrual periods, has led to the idea that they are fearful of growing up and wish to deny their sexuality, remaining as children. Undoubtedly this is true in a number of cases and there is always some conflict situation, but the reasons differ for each adolescent and have to be explored individually. In such exploration, parents have a vital role to play. They have to be patient and understanding and, at the same time, aware that often there is some lack of insight in this illness, so that the teenager may not always realise how much they need help. The most important task in treatment is for the patient and the relatives to reach a full understanding of why this starvation has come about. It is not sufficient for food intake to be pushed until the patient reaches a reasonably normal weight. This may result in pounds being lost just as rapidly when they are discharged, so the condition becomes a chronic one extending over a number of years, the individual leading a life totally dominated by food or the deprivation of it.

Bulimia nervosa

This is the term used to describe a condition characterised by recurrent episodes of binge eating, followed by self-induced vomiting and purging with laxatives. Unlike anorexia nervosa, the weight is usually maintained at a relatively normal level by these means. During a binge there is a rapid consumption of foods, especially carbohydrates, in a short space of time. There is a feeling of loss of control during binges and sufferers may even take piles of frozen food from the freezer and consume this, if nothing else is available. There is regular self-induced vomiting and the abuse of laxatives, dietary restriction at other times and vigorous exercises to prevent weight gain. The condition is said to be present when there are at least two binges per week over a period of three months. There is a persistent over-concern with body weight and shape. The male:female ratio is 1:10 and the disorder is estimated to affect 2–5 per cent of young women in the West. Often the adolescent has attempted to diet to lose weight, but then hunger has forced them to binge on forbidden foods. The intolerable fullness leads to nausea and vomiting which thus appears to offer a way of eating as much as desired without gaining weight. The condition is often associated with depression.

In severe cases there may be tell-tale physical signs. The constant vomiting causes the enamel of the surface of the teeth to be eroded, sometimes to a marked degree. The fact that the fingers are frequently pushed down the throat to induce vomiting leads to the formation of hard skin on the back of the hands and there may be absence of periods in females, who form the vast majority of sufferers. Dietary deficiencies can lead to fatigue, lassitude, and swelling of the legs and feet, particularly where body minerals are being excreted through the abuse of laxatives.

Obviously there are profound psychological disturbances which lead to such behaviour and, in particular, a morbid fear of fatness and an abnormal preoccupation with body size and shape. It may commence after some traumatic event such as an unhappy love affair or sexual assault, and is perpetuated by the vicious cycle of binge eating-dietary restriction, vomiting, and laxatives-further drop in self-esteem-comfort binge eating. Since, on the whole, most patients remain at a near normal weight, the condition may be undetected for long periods of time.

It is a condition which requires expert treatment at a specialised clinic. Good results have been reported from psychological treatments. These are directed in various ways. Firstly, there should be education about the harmful effects of bingeing and purging upon the body. Many individuals do not appreciate the physiological changes brought about by prolonged vomiting and diarrhoea. Secondly, behavioural treatment is used to regulate and normalise food intake, giving a balanced diet of enough calories to maintain the current weight. The individual has to try to avoid both the stimuli which lead to binges and any exposure to forbidden foods, and to assume responsibility for their own eating behaviour. With practice, many bulimics can avoid bingeing by understanding the impulses that make them do it and by talking to someone about it. Certain thoughts common in this condition need to be corrected, such as, 'If I do not lose weight, I will be a bad person.' Thirdly, the basic underlying causes have to be explored, faulty relationships repaired, and self-esteem restored.

5

SEXUAL DEVELOPMENT

There are probably few subjects that parents find more difficult to approach with a teenager than the whole question of sexual development. Many of them were themselves raised by parents who retained rigid ideas about sexuality in conformity with society's expectations, even if the reality was somewhat different. The fact that sex was frequently a taboo subject in the home, together with the mores that dictated that there must be virginity prior to marriage, especially for girls, the disgrace of conceiving a child outside wedlock, and the frequent ignorance about even the most elementary sexual functions, combined to produce considerable unhappiness.

Parents often feel that they lack the knowledge, vocabulary, and practice to speak about sexual matters comfortably. They may be conscious of the fact that, not surprisingly, they are confused about certain sexual values such as the advisability of premarital sex or the ethics of abortion. They are aware that discussions about sex may require them to talk about their own experiences or to express judgements about controversial matters. Frequently they are torn between being regarded as 'old-fashioned and fuddy-duddy' or excessively 'liberal'. Sexual topics generate strong feelings in most people and parents may become conscious of their own sexual dissatisfactions or disappointments in talking to their children. Moreover, children often collude in the avoidance of sexual discussions, since to talk with parents about sex implies that one is too interested in it and, at the same time, ignorant about it. So they may resist talking to parents even when the latter take the initiative. It is important, therefore, that both parents and children should be used to talking naturally about sexual topics from an early age, since it is most usually at puberty that such inhibitions begin.

SEX EDUCATION

It is vital that children should be aware of the changes that will take place in their bodies *before* they actually occur and that their questions are truthfully answered in a way they can understand. Amazingly enough, one still sometimes encounters teenage girls to whom the onset of menstruation comes as a complete and disturbing surprise, and a number of adolescents who have only a very rudimentary knowledge of the whole anatomy of their sexual organs. Such education should not be left to the schools, but should be seen as part of parental responsibility. Parents should, in particular, try to overcome any reticence or embarrassment that they may have about discussing sexual matters with their children, since this will be readily communicated to the teenagers, making them shy to ask questions about things that trouble them.

It is interesting to realise that a considerable number of young people still retain many erroneous concepts about sexual matters, such as the idea that pregnancy cannot occur on the first occasion of sexual intercourse or during menstruation or that sexually transmitted diseases can be acquired from lavatory seats. Such misconceptions can lead to unwarranted risks being taken or, sometimes, to preoccupations with ideas that a quite innocent activity has led to a venereal infection.

However, sexual intercourse is more than an instinctive or mechanical act. It is invested with considerable emotional significance and never more so than for teenagers who are, by nature, both explorative and romantic. All parents will have developed their own attitudes about sexual matters based upon their beliefs and experience. They will obviously wish to convey these to the adolescent, but at the same time they must accept that the teenager has to decide for themselves what is best for them. What is vitally important is that this should be an informed choice, not one based upon ignorance. Inadequate sexual information can lead to an unplanned pregnancy and possible abortion or the development of a sexually related illness, which may have considerable long-term effects on health and fertility. For example, although the parents may have a belief in premarital chastity, they cannot necessarily expect that an adolescent will accept these views. They should, therefore, be prepared to ensure that contraceptive advice is available to a boy or girl who is sexually active. On the other hand, they should not assume that teenagers wish to indulge in sexual intercourse at every possible opportunity, a view often reinforced by the media and not one borne out by what is known about adolescent sexuality. In short, parents have the difficult task of adjusting to what is really happening in a practical way.

EARLY LOVE AFFAIRS

Teenagers may develop emotional attachments to members of their own sex, as discussed later in this chapter. This may be particularly marked where there is little opportunity for contact with the opposite sex. Usually such attachments do not last very long and need not be a matter for concern, providing they do not affect normal life. Nor does such an attachment indicate that the adolescent will not proceed to a heterosexual orientation. Sometimes there is an idealisation of an older person such as a film or pop star. Usually the phase will pass within months and the parents should react tolerantly and without ridicule. They should see this phase as a testing period for more permanent and reliable attachments. Teenagers should be given the opportunity to work through their conflicting feelings and are often able to learn considerably about emotional relationships by this type of 'playing' at sexuality with someone who is unattainable.

Where there is security and affection within the home, early love affairs with members of the peer group are usually conducted in a spirit of friendship and camaraderie rather than too intensely. However, an unhappy adolescent may well cling to a boy- or girlfriend who shows them affection, even though the relationship is not one which can last and is taken more lightly by the other partner. Often such a partner cannot cope with this intensity of feeling and breaks away, sometimes quite abruptly, because they are too inexperienced to handle the situation. Such rejection may lead to a suicide attempt as a way of getting the loved one to return. Parents can try to prevent such a situation by making the teenager feel wanted and valued by them, so that they are not desperate for the love of others. Particularly, they should emphasise that the adolescent is attractive and can have a choice of a wide circle of friends. Moreover, they should point out that to try to obtain affection by any type of emotional blackmail is doomed to end in failure. The majority of ex-boy- or ex-girlfriends do not return because of a suicidal gesture, which additionally may have unforeseen serious physical consequences; if they do return temporarily, out of a sense of guilt, the relationship does not last.

Parents should also try not to interfere in the adolescent's relationships in the sense of making joking or sarcastic remarks, even if these are well-meaning. Many teenagers are very sensitive about their developing sexual feelings, are insecure, even if they do not ostensibly appear so, and may become inhibited by adult comments in what could be a very rewarding friendship.

CONTRACEPTION

Parents will naturally wish to make their views on premarital sexual relationships clear to their children. There are a number of arguments which may make early commencement of sexual relations unwise, not least of which is the fact that the adolescent may not be sufficiently emotionally mature to deal with the problems that may arise and the possibility of such a relationship ending sometimes one-sidedly. Adolescence can also be viewed as a time for both learning and having fun, without the need for complete commitment to one person. However, parents are rarely in the position of forbidding or preventing a sexual relationship, even if they wish to do so. They have to rely upon the background that they have given the teenager from childhood to enable them to make wise judgements. Although sex by its very nature produces spontaneous and powerful emotions, teenagers should not be encouraged to think that these emotions cannot be controlled or made the subject of rational decisions. In particular, some care needs to be exercised to ensure that a teenager is not put in a situation, as for example being under the influence of drugs or alcohol, where they are not fully aware of what they are doing.

The worst scenario is when a teenage girl becomes pregnant because she is afraid to discuss a sexual relationship with her parents and is too ignorant or ashamed to seek contraceptive advice. Probably the two most accepted methods of contraception for teenagers, and the safest, are the condom (sheath) and the pill. The latter, because it supplies oestrogen and progesterone hormones, so raising their levels in the blood, inhibits ovulation. However, it has to be taken regularly as prescribed and its absorption can be affected by conditions which cause vomiting or diarrhoea and by certain antibiotics. It may well be that a girl feels that she cannot seek advice from her family doctor, for a variety of reasons, although it is hoped that teenagers will feel sufficient confidence to do so. However, contraceptive advice is freely available from any local family planning clinic where doctors specialise in advising on the most appropriate methods for each individual.

Mention should also be made of the 'morning after pill' which contains both oestrogen and progesterone and which, if given early enough in the cycle, inhibits ovulation or, if taken after ovulation, prevents implantation of the fertilised ovum. This pill has to be administered within 72 hours after unprotected intercourse. Other contraceptive measures, such as withdrawal prior to ejaculation or the use of spermicides (foam or jelly inserted into the vagina to inhibit the spermatozoa in the seminal fluid), are not nearly so effective and should not be relied upon as methods of contraception, unless such spermicides are used in conjunction with a mechanical barrier such as a condom or an intravaginal diaphragm. It is hoped, moreover, that in adolescent sexual relationships, as in adult ones, responsibility for contraception should be a matter for both sexes, and discussed openly.

PREGNANCY

An unplanned pregnancy for a teenage girl can have many serious consequences. It can interfere with her education or work training and impose upon her a long-term responsibility for another human life. It may also cause her to make a hasty marriage, which both she and her partner will come to resent. This is not to say that some such teenage marriages do not work out well, but, unfortunately, statistics show that this is the exception rather than the rule because of the immaturity of both individuals.

Although abortion is now freely available, it is never an easy decision for girls to take. Some will feel that they cannot consider this option and will wish to continue with the pregnancy. Some will have no doubt that abortion is the best way out of the situation. Others, possibly the majority, find the decision an extremely difficult one to make. Parents may feel that they know what is best, but they must not force their views upon the teenager. They should, in particular, avoid adopting an attitude of blame or the view that a pregnancy is a shameful thing. Whilst it is self-evident that, if a decision is made to have an abortion, the earlier it is carried out the better, the adolescent must be given time to come to terms with the situation and their feelings so that they are not left with guilt and regrets. They may find it beneficial to talk to a counsellor at one of the specialist agencies listed at the end of this book. Such agencies exist, not to enforce one view or the other, but to enable bewildered women to decide what is the best in all their particular circumstances. What is also important is that a pregnancy should be diagnosed as soon as possible and not hidden, so that a decision can be made. If the teenager has decided to continue with the pregnancy in a full appraisal of all the circumstances, the parents should offer her their full support and care. It is better that she should be with them rather than in a home for unmarried mothers where she is with strangers, no matter how caring. Where there has been a long-lasting relationship between a couple, the teenage father may also be confused and bewildered about his responsibilities. If both wish to continue their relationship this should be encouraged, but time has to be allowed to see if such an attachment can work out as a permanent one.

SEXUAL ORIENTATION

In these days of widespread publicity about sexual matters, a number of teenagers are confused about aspects of their sexuality, not least about their own sexual identity. Parents should avoid compounding this confusion by an insistence upon sexual stereotypes, for instance that boys are cissies if they do not enjoy playing with guns and cars and that girls have to be involved in so-called feminine pursuits such as playing with dolls and dressing in pretty frilly clothes. Many adolescents pass through a stage in which their emotional attachment is to someone of the same sex. However, the majority go on to a heterosexual orientation.

Discussion with many homosexuals reveals that they have realised that their emotional attachment is to their own sex from an early age. They have as little sexual interest in the opposite sex as a heterosexual would have in a person of the same sex. It is recognised that homosexuality cannot be changed by any type of therapy, even if this were regarded as desirable, and that, at the present time, the whole concept of sexual orientation is imperfectly understood. Parents should accept, if this is the case, that their child is homosexual. There may be those teenagers, however, who are unsure for various reasons about their sexual identity and counselling groups exist to help them with their difficulties. One thing clear from all the studies is that sexual orientation, once firmly established, cannot be altered and to attempt to do so is to create considerable unhappiness for the individual and for those with whom they become emotionally involved.

47

SEXUAL ABUSE

It has recently become clear that sexual abuse of children by adults and sometimes even by teenagers, who have themselves been abused, is more common than previously thought. Young children are afraid to protest because the abuser is usually a close member of the family and because they feel that they have in some way been responsible for the abuse. Under some circumstances, the abuse may be regarded by the child as 'normal'. A teenager who suffers sexual abuse for the first time may well protest, although this is not necessarily so since they too may feel ashamed, frightened, and uncertain of adult response. Unfortunately, where the abuse is of long standing, the child may suffer in silence into the teenage years. The situation is often compounded by the fact that the abuser is frequently a relative or a close family friend who has been in a position of trust.

The harm that sexual abuse causes to the abused individual is incalculable. Many abused individuals who do not receive help go on to become abusers themselves and have extreme difficulty in making adult emotional relationships. It is also a misapprehension that it is only girls who are sexually abused. Evidence shows that boys are in equal danger. Parents need to be conscious that it could happen to their child, that child abusers are frequently those who would be least suspected, and that children must be made aware of the dangers in a calm and non-frightening way. Teenagers are, on the whole, of an age to be more perceptive of such possibilities, but even then the reticence of some parents in bringing up sexual matters with them may make it difficult for them to speak openly.

Sexual abuse should be suspected if the teenager becomes withdrawn, moody, and has symptoms such as discharge, pain, or bleeding which might indicate genital or rectal interference. There may be frequent washing since the adolescent feels contaminated. The teenager may attempt to avoid a particular situation where the abuse is likely to occur. With patience, they will often be ready to talk about the abuse, as witness the immense response to Childline, the national telephone help line set up for abuse victims by TV presenter Esther Rantzen. If a parent suspects abuse, they should immediately consult a professional, and I suggest that one of the counselling services listed at the end of this book or the family doctor could be the first to be approached. Whilst one does not wish to encourage unreasonable suspicions, this is a matter too serious to be ignored and one with potentially long-term consequences.

SEXUAL VIOLENCE

A teenager has to be helped to avoid potentially dangerous situations by being made aware that such possibilities exist, since it is a common human attitude that 'it cannot happen to me'. Young teenagers should not be expected to walk home alone late at night or to hitch lifts from strangers. It is not necessary to fill their minds with innumerable fears about every situation, but it is equally foolish not to issue sensible warnings about the ways in which they can be exploited. Parents should be aware of where the adolescents are going and who they are with, and, if they are going away, should have confirmation and their address and phone number.

In this connection too, mention should be made of hard pornographic and sexually violent videos which have, in a very small minority of youngsters, become an addition. By such videos I mean those which show scenes of rape, child abuse, and cruelty inflicted as a means of sexual gratification. Far from being a harmless substitute for real violence, the evidence is that they encourage an attitude of mind which seeks to act out what has been witnessed and to proceed to more extreme activity. Particularly with younger teenagers, parents should ensure that they are not viewing such videos and, at the same time, encourage the attitude that sexual activity involves affection, tenderness, and respect for the other person.

6

PROBLEMS AT SCHOOL

Two fairly common and major problems amongst adolescents attending school are *school refusal* and *truancy*. A distinction has to be made between them since the causes, and hence the ways in which they should be dealt with, are very different.

SCHOOL REFUSAL

The adolescent begins gradually to refuse to go to school, often making complaints of illness in order to stay at home. Such teenagers have usually achieved high standards at school and, whilst school refusal may be associated with problems such as bullying, more usually the adolescent is not so much afraid of going to school as of leaving home.

School refusal can be due to a variety of reasons. There may indeed be difficulties at school which need investigation. Moreover, the adolescent may be experiencing stresses within themselves which make the formation of peer relationships difficult. There may be new fears about travelling, sitting in crowded classrooms, or tests for which they are unprepared. Some adolescents are nervous of exposing their bodies when undressing for physical activities, and avoid school on those days.

However, in many cases school refusal is related to problems perceived at home. The teenager may feel that they have to stay away from school in order to protect a mother from violence or to care for a single parent who is mentally or physically ill. In extreme cases, such a child may take over most of the nursing care and, where a mother is severely incapacitated by depression or other psychiatric illness, may also adopt the role of the one who deals with all the authorities such as the DSS. Alternatively, the adolescent may be very worried about parental disagreements and fear that, if they leave home, the parents will separate and disappear for ever. They see their presence as the thing that keeps the parents together.

Sometimes, there is jealousy of a younger sibling whom the adolescent feels is getting all the attention and they may cast themselves into a sick role in order to gain more attention and affection. This can occur particularly when there is a genuine invalid or even a terminally ill brother or sister. At such times the healthy teenager feels a complex of emotions – guilt about being well, jealousy of the extra attention the sick sibling is getting, more guilt about these resentments, and fear that death may occur when they are at school and are not able to say goodbye.

Teenagers who refuse to go to school or make excuses to stay away are, on the whole, compliant and well-behaved in other respects. Often the cause of school refusal will be fairly obvious and the problem can be dealt with by talking about it and about the teenager's feelings. An important factor in dealing with school refusal is that it should not be allowed to develop into an intractable problem. Where the adolescent has not been to school for a number of months, it becomes extremely difficult to persuade them to return, particularly as it is physically impossible to get them there unless they are willing to co-operate. Parents should not collude with absences from school. Unfortunately, some parents who are lonely or unhappy do precisely this in order to have company and help in the house.

Complaints each morning about physical symptoms should lead to the suspicion that there is a problem. If persistent, these symptoms should be investigated and, if no organic cause is found, an attempt should be made to discover the psychological factors leading to school refusal. It is not sufficient merely to insist on a return to school because the teenager has no recognisable illness, since this will only lead to a recurrence and the display of other symptoms. Parents should not, on the other hand, be too ready to jump to the conclusion that the physical complaints are not genuine. A colleague of mine with psychiatric nursing training was disconcerted to learn that, having sent her 13-year-old off to school in the belief that his complaints of abdominal pain were designed only to avoid doing a forthcoming test, he had been admitted to hospital with acute appendicitis. Parents cannot win!

TRUANCY

The truant usually leaves home for school at the appropriate time and returns in similar fashion. In between, they are neither at home nor at school and are, therefore, easily drawn into anti-social activities such as petty theft, shoplifting or drug taking. The truants, on the whole, form a rather different group to the school refusers. They tend to be poor achievers educationally and, because of this, often find school work boring and feel teachers take little interest in them. They are frequently un-disciplined and difficult in other ways and there may be lack of any parental control. They often begin truanting because they fall in with a gang who is doing the same. There is sometimes a breakdown in communication between parents and child, so that the child cannot confess difficulties to them.

It may be difficult for parents to detect that their child is truanting. However, they should be alerted by a lack of aca-demic progress and by the behaviour of the adolescent's friends. Most teenagers have homework in which parents should take an interest and they should be concerned if none is being done. Contact with the school, if parents are suspicious, should provide evidence of non-attendance. Truanting usually occurs after a long period of feeling hopeless about school. It is certainly understandable that an adolescent, who is consistently bottom in every subject and to whom it is made clear that they can never hope to pass any examinations, feels it is much more pleasant to wander around the High Street shops. Parents should try never to allow a child to get into that situation, by helping them with subjects they find difficult, encouraging other talents that they have, and laying emphasis upon the positive benefits of enjoyment of learning. It is a sad fact that a number of teenagers leave school unable even to read a simple book, so it is not to be wondered at that vast areas of knowledge are meaningless to them.

In a minority of cases truanting may not be unproductive. Teenagers with a special talent may abscond from school in order to pursue interests in art, music, or sport, and parents then have to consider how such talents can be most effectively developed within the normal school framework.

Leaving aside such situations, truanting, particularly in adolescents in the 14–16 age group, can be very difficult to control since by that time many of them have fallen irremedi-ably behind with their school work. This means that they have no hope of achieving even minimal academic qualifications and have extreme problems in finding any kind of employment. The pattern of their life continues to be wandering around the streets aimlessly, with all its attendant problems. Hence truanting, like school refusal, should be dealt with as promptly as possible. Parents should make it their business to liaise with the school about their child's attendance and achievements and, if there is truanting, try to deal with the causes.

BULLYING AND TEASING

Many adolescents experience some bullying occasionally, particularly when they enter a new environment such as a change of school or workplace. In some schools or workplaces bullying of a newcomer is, unfortunately, seen as a kind of primitive initiation ceremony and testing situation. The majority of those bullied in such circumstances are able to overcome this with a reasonable degree of resilience. However, bullying sometimes becomes prolonged and can affect the victim so severely as to lead to suicidal attempts or even successful suicide. Boys tend to go in for physical bullying, whilst girls often favour more subtle forms of mental torment.

Bullying becomes increasingly intolerable when the victim is in a situation from which they cannot escape. Graham Greene in his autobiography has vividly recalled the bully at his boarding school who 'practised torments with dividers', an individual whom he feels has left him with a life-long sympathy for those who are bullied in any situation. Adolescents at boarding school, whose parents can rarely visit or who are isolated by race, religion or colour, are liable to be most affected by bullying. It is often made worse when the individual is shy, sensitive, insecure, or unable to confide in anyone about it.

Tempting as it may be for parents to complain to the school about bullying, this may sometimes be counter-productive. Good teachers should, hopefully, be able to perceive bullying and prevent it, whilst complaints in situations where bullying is regarded with indifference may only rebound upon the victim. If bullying is allowed to proceed unchecked at a school, parents will have to give serious consideration to transferring their child to a more congenial establishment. Bullying which involves sexual harassment or serious physical or mental intimidation should always be brought to the attention of the school authorities so that the matter can be properly investigated. Where bullying takes the form of excessive teasing and/or ridicule, parents have to devote their attention to helping the victim handle the situation.

53

Teenagers may often not confess to being bullied because they are ashamed about it or even frightened. Parents should suspect bullying if the adolescent is fearful of going to school, becomes anxious or depressed, shows a decline in their school work, is reluctant to talk about school activities, and has few friends. Whilst being sympathetic, they should encourage the teenager to stand up for themselves in a constructive way, to try to ignore the bullying, not to show the bully that they are concerned, and to adopt verbal and tactical strategies against the bully which will disconcert them. They should also try to encourage activities outside school which will provide happiness and satisfaction. Bullies flourish when their victims seem to be cowed and in awe of them, so the teenager should be given an insight into this situation and into the unhappy circumstances which often produce a bully. Above all, parents should always encourage the child to talk to them about their difficulties.

Parents may find it less easy to accept a situation where their child is a bully. Like so many other personality traits, this can begin with childhood upbringing. If a child is brought up to despise others because of their race, colour, or religion, it is hardly surprising that they pick upon such individuals at school. For a teenager who is not particularly successful, this may provide a way out of acknowledging their own deficiencies especially when they have faulty parental examples.

The supreme ones must be the mother who was complaining that her child could not get into the school football team because 'it was full of nig nogs' or the father who pointed to a clever child with a stumbling gait due to mild cerebral palsy and said, 'It's a crime to let a cripple like that go to a normal school.' Parents should teach their children a tolerant and compassionate attitude to other human beings and to animals from an early age and, even more importantly, carry it out in their own life. They should realise that physical force and bullying are not a solution to life's problems, and should make it clear that aggressive behaviour is not acceptable. Nor should they adopt a bullying attitude to their children, since teenagers tend to model themselves, albeit often unconsciously, upon their parents.

The bully is frequently obtaining relief from unhappiness by venting venom upon others, whom he or she perceives to be weak and vulnerable. The power that they can obtain over such people may become a great source of perverted satisfaction. Persistent and unchecked bullying can lead to the development of sadistic behaviour in later life. Parents who discover that their child is a bully should endeavour to understand the reasons for this. They cannot hope to stop bullying by merely issuing an edict that it should not occur or by punishment, which only confirms the bully in the belief that 'might is right'. They should attempt to alter the attitudes that have led to the situation and to give the bully an understanding of how their victims must feel about them. For example, if the bully says 'X is such a cissy', it is not out of order to point out that they, the bully, have things they are afraid of as well. Again, one should try to divert aggression into acceptable outlets such as sports. Older siblings who are encouraging bullying should be firmly dissuaded from this. Parental attitudes are very important to teenagers, even though they may not acknowledge this fact, so parents should stand firm in their disapproval of bullying and not allow the bully to take refuge in excuses or in what they may perceive as tacit parental approval.

SHYNESS AND INABILITY TO MAKE FRIENDS

Shyness can be a serious problem for some teenagers, particularly in early adolescence where there is a tendency, especially amongst girls, to have 'best friends' with others being rejected. Those who have difficulty in making friends should be encouraged to try to take an interest in others and not to be constantly introspective about themselves and the effect they are having on those around them. They should also be helped to be independent and self-sufficient, so that they are not unduly cast down if a friendship does not develop. Things are often easier for the shy individual if they can talk readily to their parents and feel they are accepted at home. However, the parents should not be tempted to try to take the place of friends in the teenager's own peer group and should actively encourage outside interests.

CRUSHES

Intense emotional attachments to unattainable individuals are a normal part of adolescence. They are a preparation for real-life relationships and are usually harmless. The beloved may be an older adolescent, a film or pop star or an older adult of the teenager's acquaintance. Usually, there is worship from afar, idealisation, and fantasies about what the relationship might be like. Occasionally however, there may be a serious attempt to bring the fantasy into reality. An adolescent girl may make advances to a male teacher or a friend of the family. Such situations may be, at the least, embarrassing and may sometimes lead to an active sexual involvement. How the parents should react naturally depends upon all the circumstances, for example, the age of the teenager, the caring nature of the relationship, and whether there is any evidence that the adolescent is being exploited.

More rarely, the teenager, usually a girl, tries to live out her fantasy in a completely unrealistic way. She begins to maintain that a pop star, for example, has asked her to marry him, tells her friends that she is engaged to him or even that she is expecting his baby. She may even go to the extent of purchasing an engagement ring or wedding ring to lend credence to her story. Such fantasies often occur in those who feel they are unattractive to more accessible members of the opposite sex or who wish to be accepted enthusiastically by their peer group. In some cases they may be the forerunner of a serious psychiatric illness. They should always be taken seriously and professional advice sought.

THE GIFTED TEENAGER

A very clever child may find there is a gulf between their intellectual and emotional development. They may be ill at ease with their own peer group and unable to deal with those who are their contemporaries in intellectual ability. They may be teased because they are seen as different. Because of all these factors, they are often very close to their parents who frequently form an active source of encouragement. On occasions, a child of high intelligence may be regarded as naughty because they are readily bored by the school work which they have already mastered and so play around in class. However, assessment of intellectual ability will soon establish whether this is the cause of such behaviour. Naturally, gifted children have to be given every opportunity to develop their skills, but, at the same time, they should be helped to have friends of their own age with whom they can pursue normal adolescent activities. This avoids the tendency to social isolation which can make relationships difficult for them in later life. Most importantly, they should be encouraged to realise that their skill is a special gift to be valued, but not something which makes them superior to others who are less intelligent.

THE SLOW LEARNER

Parents will usually be aware from an early age that their child has learning difficulties and, therefore, they will already be receiving special education for their particular needs. A sudden failure to learn in the early teenage years may be due to emotional difficulties, physical illness, or to factors which can be easily remedied such as short-sightedness manifesting itself at puberty and leading to an inability to see distant things clearly. Any abrupt deterioration in school attainment should be investigated to discover the cause.

Slow learners can have special emotional problems when they reach adolescence. They may become upset because they realise that they are not on an intellectual par with their peers and may be bullied and teased by other uncaring, more quick-witted teenagers. They may also face employment difficulties. It is natural that parents should wish to protect such vulnerable adolescents, but this is not always in their best interests. They have to learn to cope with life outside the family circle and parents should encourage them to develop social skills which make acceptance within their peer group easier. Moreover, they should concentrate upon the particular aptitudes that the adolescent has. For example, a young patient of mine who had great difficulty with any school subjects had a talent for flower arranging which soon made her in great demand on many social occasions and assured her a wide circle of friends.

PROBLEMS OF THE BOARDER

Many teenagers settle down well at boarding school, most of which are vastly different from the spartan institutions of the past. For a minority of adolescents bullying and homesickness are problems. Before deciding upon boarding school education, consideration has to be given to the individual teenager and their special needs. A school which places great emphasis upon sport and physical achievement is not likely to be the most suitable for an adolescent who is hopeless at any games and whose talents lie within the sphere of music, art, and literature. Moreover, certain personalities will prefer the quietude of life as a day pupil to the enforced gregariousness of boarding. Many parents and adolescents feel that weekly boarding with weekends spent at home is a good compromise.

If bullying is such a problem that it does not respond to reasonable measures, in my opinion the child should be removed to a different school. There can be few situations more destructive than to be constantly afraid and insecure.

Homesickness can usually be dealt with by regular communications and, where possible, frequent visits home. The adolescent should never be allowed to feel that they have been sent away from home in order to get rid of them or for the convenience of the parents. They should always take with them some mementoes of home and be kept in constant touch with the family. Never accept any advice that tells you that it is much better not to write or telephone for a few weeks, because this will help the teenager to adjust. This used to be the attitude in hospitals for children, until it was amply demonstrated how traumatic this was and how deserted the young patients felt. Because a teenager may get upset at receiving a letter from home, it does not mean that they should not have them. They need to feel that their parents love and think about them. In the final analysis, if a teenager becomes progressively more unhappy at boarding school, every effort should be made to return to a day school placement. A number of adolescents, particularly at the age of 13 or 14, still need the security that living at home can bring and there is no need to feel that they are abnormal in any way because they have this attitude.

DISCIPLINE PROBLEMS AT SCHOOL

Many teenagers protest vociferously about what they see as unfair punishments: 'We all had to stay in because X and Y talked in the class,' etc. Such perceived unfairnesses are usually quickly forgotten, but it is much more serious when the adolescent feels that their honesty or integrity has been impugned. Most teenagers have a strong sense of fair play and nothing is more hurtful to them, at home or at school, than to be wrongly accused, particularly if they feel that they have not had a fair hearing. Terence Rattigan demonstrated this in his play *The Winslow Boy*, where a naval cadet is wrongfully expelled for stealing and is only exonerated by the steadfast efforts of his father.

Parents should always listen to the explanations of their children if the latter are suspected of some wrongdoing. A teenage patient of mine, who admitted to various misdemeanours such as shoplifting and driving stolen cars, was extremely upset when his parents did not believe that he was innocent of a charge of trying to seduce a 13-year-old girl at his school. 'I know I'm a bit of a bad lot,' he said, 'but I would never take advantage of someone as young as that.' One of the things that teenagers most remember and resent are the times when they have been punished for offences that they did not commit.

Adolescents should be made aware of the fact that they need to conform to school rules. If they feel those rules are excessively restrictive, they should be able to point this out to those in charge. They should also realise the need for certain regulations: for example being at school on time, presenting homework on the date it is due, not creating a disturbance in class, and so on. Where there have been serious breaches of discipline, parents should ask to see the evidence that their child is implicated. They should talk to the child, try to ascertain the facts, and if the evidence is conclusive, they must accept it. However, they should also ensure that their child is not being made a scapegoat for someone who has escaped correction. As I have stated previously, nothing is more hurtful than an unjust punishment. In such circumstances it is vital that the adolescent feels that they can talk freely and honestly to their parents.

7

DRUG ABUSE

This is becoming an increasing problem amongst adolescents and is, quite rightly, a matter for grave concern. What may begin as an experiment, out of bravado and a desire to copy the peer group, may end with addiction, fatal overdose, illnesses such as hepatitis B or AIDS from shared needles, and the development of serious psychiatric disturbances necessitating hospitalisation. Parents should advise their children about these dangers early on in their life, since substance abuse can, under certain circumstances, begin at an early age. They should also endeavour not to display to the youngsters their own particular addictions, which they may regard as socially acceptable, such as heavy cigarette smoking and drinking. Many adolescents who experiment with cannabis, LSD, and so on, will argue that adults use substances such as nicotine and alcohol which are just as harmful.

NICOTINE

Whilst cigarette smoking may not appear to fall into the same category as heroin or cocaine addiction, it is a potent cause of premature mortality from chest and heart ailments and cancers of the lungs, mouth, and throat. It is estimated that tobacco contributes to at least 100,000 premature deaths in the UK every year (far more than other addictions). Once established as a habit, it becomes increasingly difficult to break. There is evidence that increasing numbers of girls are smoking, with nearly a quarter being smokers by the age of 15, compared with 17 per cent of boys of the same age. Children are more likely to smoke if the parents are smokers and a recent Health Education Council survey indicated that child smokers are more likely to take illegal drugs. Clearly it is a worrying problem. Parents should endeavour to prevent teenagers from starting to smoke cigarettes by their own example and by emphasising the disadvantages. The argument that prolonged smoking leads to serious damage to the body may not weigh very heavily in the adolescent mind, but they may be more susceptible to the fact that smoking makes their hair, clothes, and breath smell and discolours their teeth and fingers. Many adolescents begin smoking because it relieves stress and tension to a certain extent or because they are bored, since nicotine acts as a stimulant. Some girls smoke because it reduces their appetite and so aids maintenance of a slim figure.

ALCOHOL

Alcoholic drinks consist chiefly of water and ethyl alcohol, produced by the fermentation of fruits, vegetables, or grains, in varying proportions, with spirits such as gin, whisky, and vodka containing the highest percentage of alcohol. At the age of 18 teenagers can drink at the bar and buy alcohol in a pub or off-licence. It is an offence to knowingly sell alcohol to anyone under the age of 18. It is also an offence to drive whilst under the influence of drink or with more than 80 mgs of alcohol in every 100 mls of blood. The rate at which the blood alcohol reaches this limit varies according to the amount of food ingested, the rapidity with which the alcohol has been taken, and the type and strength of the alcohol. What is certain is that even small amounts of alcohol impair the fine judgement and manual dexterity required to drive a car or motor cycle; and so it should be made a rule that alcohol should not be consumed when driving. It has to be emphasised to teenagers, who obviously are less experienced on the road and therefore more prone to accidents from a variety of causes, that about a third of drivers and up to a quarter of all adult pedestrians killed in road accidents have blood alcohols above the legal limit.

Teenagers tend to drink in groups and may consume large amounts of alcohol due to peer pressure or unawareness of the effects that alcohol can have. They should normally confine their drinking to one or two drinks a day and not make a habit of regular drinking. Part of the problem with heavy drinking is the fact that it destroys inhibitions and releases aggressive behaviour. Youngsters who would normally be law-abiding may get into fights and be arrested for being drunk and disorderly. Moreover, alcohol in large doses is a cerebral depressant. Very high blood levels of alcohol lead to unconsciousness and finally death from respiratory paralysis. With increasing levels of alcohol intake there is a danger of choking on vomit whilst unconscious or of falling down and sustaining a severe or fatal injury.

Addiction to alcohol may begin in the teenage years and is characterised by increasing alcohol consumption. There may be symptoms of withdrawal, such as hangovers, occurring when there is an abrupt fall in the alcohol level, and a growing absorption in activities which involve drinking, such as drinking at lunchtime and spending as much time as possible in the pub. Many individuals become dependent upon alcohol because it temporarily relieves anxiety and depression. A teenager who, for example, cannot find work and has difficulty with inter-personal relationships may well seek consolation in heavy drinking. The effect of this is, ultimately, only to increase depression and social inadequacy and so more alcohol is taken.

Occasionally parents may find that the adolescent tends to drink at home, using the family liquor supply and then re-plenishing the bottle with water. The father of one such teenager was astonished, as he offered drinks to his guests from what he considered was a bottle of gin, to see them all politely sip with varying degree of surprise, until he realised his own drink contained nothing but water. Sympathetic understanding, not anger, is important when parents become aware that a teenager is finding alcohol a problem. Reproaching them will only lead to an increased desire to drink to 'escape from it all' and to secret drinking. The parents should help the teenager to deal with the difficulties that are troubling them in a construc-tive way, by allowing them to talk about the problem in order to find a solution. Where there is serious anxiety or depression which cannot be dealt with in this way, professional advice should be sought, since management of the underlying condi-tion may be necessary. Help with problem drinking can also be obtained from one of the organisations listed at the end of this book.

In preventing situations where there is a danger of excessive acute alcoholic ingestion, measures should be taken to ensure that youngsters are not drinking unsupervised under conditions where alcohol is in plentiful supply. Parents should discreetly try to make sure they are at hand if a party is being given in their home, should supply ample soft drinks and offer a bed for the night for any youngster who has had a little too much to drink. It is better to run the gauntlet of disapproving comments from the teenager such as 'surely, you don't have to be around', rather than run the risk of some youngster being seriously ill or driving home drunk. When teenagers are going out to parties, some limits as to timing should be set for the younger ones and parents should insist that they come to meet them. In the case of older teenagers, it is tempting providence for them to go off in a car, unless a parent can be absolutely certain that the driver is not going to drink. It is much wiser for parents to drive them to the party and meet them. By the time they leave home and are acting independently, the teenagers should be in a position to understand how important it is to control their drinking. In this, as in so many areas, parental example is all-important.

TRANQUILLISERS

These drugs, notably the benzodiazepines such as Valium, Librium, and Ativan, are used to control anxiety and tension. They can only be supplied on prescription and are used by doctors for anxious patients, although less so now because of the risk of dependency. In my opinion, tranquillisers should not be prescribed for teenagers unless it is absolutely necessary and then only for the shortest possible length of time. They do not solve the underlying difficulties which have caused the anxieties in the first place and may, by inducing a false sense of calm, prevent such difficulties being tackled. They also produce tolerance to their effects, so that doses have to be constantly increased. Bodily dependence can also develop, with with-drawal symptoms such as insomnia, increased anxiety and irritability when the drugs are stopped after prolonged use.

Teenagers rarely become addicted to tranquillisers, but may use them, if they have access, in time of crisis. It is not uncommon for a depressed teenager to make a suicide attempt using tranquillisers taken from a parental supply and washed down with alcohol. Coma and respiratory depression are reached more quickly if benzodiazepines and alcohol are combined. Moreover, at lower dosage levels, benzodiazepines reduce alertness and impair driving and other skills. This is obviously more marked if teenagers are taking tablets from an unauthorised supply and ingesting more than the normally prescribed dosage. Parents should ensure that any supplies of such drugs are kept secure from teenagers and they should never offer benzodiazepines to adolescents who are nervous about exams, prior to their driving test, or in any other similar circumstances. Apart from the obvious side-effects, it is a mistake to encourage the idea that all life's problems can be solved by taking pills.

HYPNOSEDATIVES

These are hypnotics intended to induce sleep and also act as sedatives to calm anxious people. Because of this latter calming effect, they are liable to produce addiction, especially in the case of the particularly efficacious ones such as barbiturates. Barbiturates include Soneryl, Sodium Amytal, Seconal, and Nembutal, and one particularly popular preparation with addicts is Drinamyl, a combination of Sodium Amytal and Dexedrine, a stimulant. Such a combination is liable to abuse because Dexedrine produces a state of excitement which is balanced by the sedative effect of the barbiturate, leading to a resultant state of euphoria.

In small doses barbiturates induce a sense of calm and relaxation; in higher doses they cause sedation. Tolerance readily develops, so that increasing dosages are needed and withdrawal symptoms can occur. Barbiturates are less common drugs of addiction than a number of others and tend to be used in combination with alcohol and amphetamines. Death from overdose can occur accidentally, since the lethal dose is close to the therapeutic dose. The effects of barbiturates are potentiated by alcohol which, in itself, decreases judgement, leading the user to forget exactly what quantity of tablets they have ingested.

AMPHETAMINES

This group of drugs are called 'speed' because they produce an increase of activity with a feeling of euphoria. They activate the user in much the same way as the body's natural adrenalin, increasing heart and breathing rate and decreasing the appetite. However, as their effect wears off there is anxiety, restlessness, depression, and insomnia. Because of their activating effect, they may be taken by sufferers from depression or by those who feel lethargic due to the onset of schizophrenia.

After prolonged use, a so-called amphetamine psychosis may develop. The user forms ideas of persecution, feeling people are plotting against them and intend them harm. They may hear voices confirming these beliefs and become agitated, excitable, and extremely disturbed. Such a condition needs psychiatric treatment.

Amphetamines are man-made powders, commonly brown or white, produced in pill or capsule form. They are usually taken by mouth, dissolved in water and injected or sniffed up the nose. The production process of amphetamine sulphate is simple and, next to cannabis, amphetamines are probably the most widely used illegal drug. The euphoriant effect quickly leads to habituation and an increased intake in order to avoid the rebound depression. Heavy use also lowers resistance to disease because of the anorectic effect and the production of insomnia. The inability to sleep may lead to barbiturate abuse for their hypnotic effect.

CANNABIS

Cannabis is made from a plant called *cannabis sativa* and has been widely smoked in many countries for generations. Estimates put the number of current users in the United Kingdom at one million, making it the most widely used of the controlled drugs. 'Hashish' or 'hash' is resin scraped from the top of the plant and compressed into hard brown blocks. 'Marijuana' and 'grass' are weaker forms of the dried plant.

Cannabis may be rolled and smoked as a cigarette, smoked in a pipe, brewed into a drink, or put into food. It has a distinctive herbal smell. The most common effects, which start a few minutes after smoking and last for up to an hour with low doses, are talkativeness, relaxation, cheerfulness and greater appreciation of colour and sound. There is a reduction in the ability to do complicated tasks, short-term memory can be affected, and there is some difficulty in concentration. Therefore, it is dangerous to drive or work machinery soon after taking cannabis.

Cannabis does not appear to produce bodily dependence, although users may begin to rely upon its relaxing effects. There is evidence, however, that prolonged inhalation of cannabis smoke can have a similar effect to tobacco upon the lungs, causing bronchitis and even lung cancer. Heavy use in some young people can produce a similar psychosis to that found in amphetamine users.

LSD – LYSERGIC ACID DIETHYLAMIDE

This is a man-made powder which, because of the minute amounts sufficient to produce a 'trip', can be particularly easily smuggled and concealed. It is a hallucinogenic drug, in other words it produces a distortion of reality. It can be taken in the form of tablets, capsules, in sugar cubes, or impregnated in paper.

One of the serious problems of LSD, which may sometimes be given surreptitiously to people at parties, is the unpredictability of its strength and effects. In a good 'trip', which begins about half an hour or so after taking the drug, there may be heightened self-awareness, a feeling that colours are stronger, a sensation of being outside one's body and ecstatic or mystical experiences. These usually reach their height within two to six hours and fade after about twelve hours. However, it is impossible to predict when an individual will have a 'bad trip'. Under these circumstances, there is a profound depression which can lead to suicide. The reality of the body image may be distorted so that the individual feels that they can fly or walk on water. Where there is associated disturbed perception of things around them, the user may think that, for example, a high building is only a few feet from the ground and jump to their death. In some individuals, the use of LSD can lead to a similar psychosis to that found with amphetamines and cannabis.

COCAINE (COKE, CRACK)

This is a white powder made from the leaves of the Andean *coca* shrub and is a powerful drug of addiction because of its stimulant effect. It can be smoked, sniffed, or injected. Its effects are to produce mental exhilaration, feelings of well-being, and an indifference to pain, tiredness, and hunger. Dependence readily develops because of the rebound sleepiness and depression, encouraging the user to take more. Prolonged use can lead to severe anxiety, insomnia, or even ideas of persecution. Contamination of the cocaine powder with other substances, as in crack, may also cause problems.

OPIATES

Morphine and codeine are pain-killing drugs produced from the opium poppy. Heroin is readily produced from morphine and in pure form is a white powder over twice as strong as morphine. It is sometimes swallowed as a tablet, sniffed up the nose like cocaine (snorting), dissolved in water and injected or smoked (chasing the dragon). It can be injected subcutaneously (skin pop), intramuscularly (fix) or intravenously (main-lining). Users often progress from oral or nasal ingestion to intravenous injections. Most of the heroin on the black market has been imported and, when sold, is usually mixed with powders of similar appearance such as talcum powder or flour.

Opiates create a detachment from reality, relieving stress and discomfort and inducing a sensation of warmth and bodily calmness. Habituation is rapid, however, and once this occurs the user will often be desperate to obtain the drug. Sudden withdrawal can cause aches, tremor, chills, sweating and muscle spasms. In prolonged use there may be apathy and reduced appetite, which are compounded by the addict's often inadequate diet and accommodation, the result of diverting more and more money to purchase increasing amounts of the drug. Considerable damage can be done by repeated injections, often with dirty needles. Overdose can also occur, leading to unconsciousness and coma. Mortality amongst opiate addicts is almost fifteen times that of the non-drug-taking population.

SOLVENTS

Solvent abuse is not uncommon because solvents are relatively easily obtained. They are carbon-based substances which are used in glues, paints, nail varnish removers, aerosols, petrol and cigarette lighter gas, most of which can be purchased in normal retail shops.

Solvent vapours are inhaled, passing from the lungs directly to the brain, to produce a feeling similar to that of being drunk. The effect can be enhanced by sniffing from the inside of a plastic bag placed over the head, so that the concentration of vapour is increased. This can be very dangerous because sniffers can become unconscious, die from asphyxia, or choke upon vomit.

Long-term solvent abuse can lead to damage to vital organs such as the brain, kidney, and liver.

Boys vastly outnumber girls in this type of substance abuse and there is often a characteristic rash over the mouth and nose.

MAGIC MUSHROOMS

A number of mushrooms can produce hallucinations. When eaten, one of the most common, the Liberty Cap, which grows wild in Britain, produces symptoms similar to that of LSD because it contains hallucinogenic chemicals. There is hilarity, overexcitement, and, with high doses, dream-like images. The greatest danger is that poisonous mushrooms may be ingested by mistake, since their appearance is very similar to the non-toxic variety.

HOW TO DETECT IF A TEENAGER IS TAKING DRUGS

It is not always easy to tell the difference between normal teenage behaviour, certain psychiatric illnesses and drug taking, especially if the latter are only taken occasionally.

However, certain types of behaviour should give cause for concern:

- loss of appetite
- uncharacteristic aggression or irritability
- sudden unexplained changes of mood
- frequent sullen, moody behaviour
- changes in sleep pattern, so that there may be insomnia or drowsiness during the day
- loss of interest in hobbies, friends, sport, or school work; decline in school work
- unusual stains, marks, smells on the body or clothes or around the house
- evidence of furtive behaviour in the form of telling lies, taking money, unexplained absences from home or selling belongings
- finding evidence of unusual powders, tablets, capsules, or empty aerosol containers.

THE DANGERS OF DRUG TAKING

A number of adolescents experiment with drugs and do not have any serious side-effects. Therefore, it is important that parents do not over-react if they discover that their child has smoked a cannabis joint or eaten a magic mushroom. However, there are many risks involved in the abuse of illegal drugs which have to be emphasised to teenagers.

- Having an accident whilst under their influence. This applies equally to alcohol as to other drugs and is made more likely by the macho image which is frequently given to beer in particular. The tragedy of killing another human being whilst driving under the influence of alcohol has a profound and lasting effect upon the teenager responsible and upon the family of the victim. Adolescents should be taught to resist any pressure which encourages them to feel that drinking large quantities of alcohol makes them more masculine. Moreover, they should also be made aware of the effect that alcohol has in decreasing inhibitions, so that after a few drinks they may feel quite capable of safe driving, when in reality they are not.

- Accidental overdose can lead to loss of consciousness, respiratory paralysis, and death. Again, it should be pointed out that many drugs distort perceptions of reality, so that the user may forget how much they have taken. With certain substances, the initial euphoria may lead to a feeling that more and more of the drug can be ingested without any serious consequences.
- Depression can lead to attempted or successful suicide.
- The teenager may progress from drugs such as cannabis to more potent ones like heroin and cocaine.
- There is a high risk of addiction or dependence after regular use.
- There can be unpleasant and potentially serious side-effects, particularly in the form of persecutory ideas, hallucinations and distortions of reality which will require, in a number of cases, hospital treatment.
- The need to satisfy the addict's craving for expensive drugs can lead to criminal behaviour such as theft, blackmail, violence or involvement in 'pushing' drugs to other people.
- The side-effects of the drugs, particularly in the case of heroin, may eventually render a normal life impossible.
- There are all the dangers of intravenous injections. Needles may not be sterile and, if shared, may become contaminated with bacteria leading to blood poisoning from which a number of addicts die. Viruses such as Hepatitis B and HIV are transmitted through blood and are, therefore, a grave risk in sharing needles. Hepatitis B can lead to liver failure and HIV to the chronic and eventually fatal AIDS. Prolonged users may run out of injectable veins and so produce abscesses, or even loss of blood supply to a limb, by accidental damage to an artery.
- Both sexes may find themselves doing things under the influence of drugs which would normally be alien to them. Again, this applies as much to alcohol, one of the most easily obtainable drugs, as to the others. There is the possibility of anti-social and criminal activity, transient sexual contact with the possibility of contracting a sexually transmitted disease and, for girls, the possibility of an unwanted pregnancy.

- The effects of these drugs vary from one individual to another and cannot be predicted. For instance, for some a drug may produce a profound depression and for others lead to a psychiatric illness very like schizophrenia.
- Being arrested for a drug offence can affect the teenager's education and career.

WHAT TO DO IF YOUR TEENAGER IS TAKING DRUGS

The above list appears daunting and it must be emphasised that only a minority of teenagers seriously abuse drugs. On the whole, abuse can be prevented by an understanding home environment, since the majority of teenagers who turn to drugs do so, as do adults, when they are feeling lonely, frustrated, bored or depressed. If they feel they can talk to their parents, they are much more likely to seek such counselling rather than resorting to drugs.

If parents suspect that their child is taking drugs, they should obviously investigate the matter thoroughly and not ignore it. They should first of all try to discover what drugs are being taken and for what reason. This should be done in a sympathetic and not reproachful way. It is important not to over-react because in this way a small problem may be made bigger. Because an adolescent has smoked a joint of cannabis or had a few too many drinks, it does not mean that they are going to end up as a hopeless addict sleeping rough on the streets. One has to remember that teenagers these days have been brought up in a culture which encourages the idea that there is a pill to cure everything and so it is not surprising that, when anxious and depressed, they feel drugs are a solution. The many bereaved people who are given Valium or Librium, as if a tranquilliser could take away the pain of the loss of a loved one, is a case in point.

It is probably wise to discuss the problem together as parents and, if in doubt, seek advice from a doctor or one of the drug counselling agencies. This will enable you to appreciate the possible dangers and side-effects of the drug(s) and is particularly important if it seems that the drug problem is a serious, long-standing one. Then the matter can be discussed with the teenager and an attempt made to understand why they need to seek refuge in drugs. The dangers of drug abuse should be emphasised in a caring, rather than authoritarian, way. At the same time, a positive approach has to be made to ameliorate the situation which has led the teenager to seek this way out and, if necessary, counselling or other treatment arranged.

If, unfortunately, it is a problem with the law that has led to the discovery of the drug abuse, you should emphasise that you will give them all possible support. If there is evidence that illegal drugs are being 'pushed' at school, work, college or in social circles, you should have no hesitation in contacting the appropriate authorities. Some adolescents, who would not normally think of taking drugs, become dependent on them because they have initially experimented with them in a group given drugs by a 'pusher' out to make money.

In summary, if drugs were taken merely out of curiosity or due to pressure from friends, an understanding talk explaining the possible dangers may well be sufficient. Many adolescents these days are reacting in a number of ways to what they see as the need for a healthier lifestyle and so emphasis should be placed upon solving problems without the aid of potentially harmful chemicals. If there is an underlying psychological problem, this should be dealt with by expert advice so that the need to rely on drugs is obviated. If there appears to be a serious drug problem, then the matter has to be broached in as tactful and understanding a way as possible, when the teenager is in a receptive mood. Contact your doctor or one of the advice centres listed at the end of this book for information about available treatment. Above all, in this situation, be patient. As anyone who has had a problem of addiction to cigarettes, alcohol or tranquillisers will appreciate, coming off addictive drugs is not easy. There may be relapses in times of stress and such teenagers need all the help and support they can get from their families.

8

BEHAVIOUR PROBLEMS

Minor degrees of deviation from what are regarded as acceptable standards of social behaviour are quite common in adolescence, as indeed at other times of life. For instance, a few half-truths may be told about a school result or the reason for being home later than usual. Such behaviour tends to be more marked when the parents have very high expectations, are critical of failure, or believe that the teenager should always be a model of perfection. On the whole, adolescents wish to please their parents and are, therefore, anxious to present as good a picture of themselves as possible. Wise parents learn to read between the lines and see both sides of the story. 'Mr X is always picking on me' may well be due to the fact that the teenager does not try very hard at Mr X's particular subject, is rather disruptive in his class, or there is a personality conflict and hence Mr X is not inclined to give him a good report. When confronted with this point of view, the honest teenager will usually grudgingly admit that it may have some validity. Moreover, parental example is very important. If the parents are seen to be lying or cheating in certain aspects of life, the teenager may assume that it is all right to follow their example.

Persistent anti-social conduct, however, should be a cause for concern and its reasons investigated before the adolescent becomes involved in serious trouble.

LYING

If a teenager is discovered to be constantly telling lies, the parents should ask themselves why the child is afraid to be truthful. It may be that they are being excessively strict and the adolescent feels that they can never meet their standards. It may indeed be the case that the rest of the teenager's peer group are being allowed to do quite reasonable activities to which their own parents object, possibly with no valid reason. The adolescent may be lying in order to join the peer group in their activities and is afraid of being stopped by their parents. Anyone who has seen the film *Dead Poets' Society* will remember the devastating effect that his father's complete denial of his acting talent and insistence that he study medicine instead had upon the American schoolboy, forcing him to lie and finally to commit suicide. The adolescent may lie in order to meet friends of which the parents disapprove. It is always unwise to forbid a teenager the company of a particular friend, since this makes the friendship all the more attractive, and this is particularly true of friendships with the opposite sex. Teenage attraction is a very powerful emotion and there can be real and painful conflict if the parents are actively hostile to such a relationship. This, of course, does not apply in cases where a teenager is obviously being taken advantage of by an older person.

Persistent lying may be an indication of the possibility of drug abuse. The user is unable to be fully truthful about their activities, has to find extra money to buy drugs, and spends time under their influence, when they should be doing other things. Lying may also be associated with truanting, since the truant is forced to give an invented account of their day at school. Anorexics will often lie about their food intake and, in tragic cases where the teenager is afraid to confess a pregnancy to the parents, lies will be told about the regularity of the menstrual periods. In other cases, lies will be told in order to obtain favour with the peer group or to appear important. For example, a teenager from a poor home attending an expensive school as a scholarship pupil may lie about the size of their parental house and their parents' income and occupation. Conversely, a law-abiding family whose child attends a school where there are a number of delinquent fathers may well discover that their child has endowed them with an undeserved criminal reputation.

Persistent lying always conceals some underlying problem or disorder which needs exploration. It has to be remembered that many teenagers have a rich Walter Mitty-type fantasy world in which they see themselves doing great things and in which they can seek refuge in times of disappointment. They are, however, able to distinguish fantasy from the often less exciting reality. In those rare cases when a child, despite parental understanding, seems unable to tell truth from fiction, psychological investigation is required.

STEALING

The motivation for stealing is not necessarily the obvious one of greed for someone else's possessions. In some circumstances an adolescent will steal quite useless and trivial trinkets, of no value, which are put into a drawer and kept secret. This often occurs when they have a feeling of being unloved or unwanted, or after a break-up between the parents, a parental desertion, or the loss of a friendship. The things stolen may provide some kind of bizarre comfort, they may represent a way of wreaking revenge on the parents by committing an anti-social act of which they would disapprove and there is often the hope that, if the theft is discovered, the parents will show increased affection and interest. The parental response to such a discovery, which often the teenager makes quite easy, should not be one of anger, which can only exacerbate the adolescent's feeling of rejection. There should be an attempt at sympathetic under-standing, since such teenagers are not going to develop into persistent thieves provided they are given the affection that they crave.

Sometimes stealing may be a form of vengeance against others by whom the teenager feels betrayed or of whom they are jealous. They may steal from a classmate who has achieved higher grades, from a sibling whom they feel is favoured, or from parents whom they feel have no interest in them. Again, the thefts are characterised, not by the monetary value of the objects stolen, but by the meaning that they have for the person from whom they have stolen. A patient of mine, for example, who considered his stepfather was unjust towards him, stole his sales order book, cut it into pieces and threw it in the river. Such thefts often involve some defacement of the object taken – an exercise book destroyed, a handkerchief cut into pieces, and so on. They are, as in the stealing of valueless trinkets, a cry for help and should be treated as such. They are frequently mani-festations of profound unhappiness and anger, and if the parents are unable to cope with the situation, professional help should be sought.

Truants are prone to steal, sometimes out of boredom and sometimes due to peer group pressure. A gang of teenagers may find it exciting to pinch things from shops, often objects of some value to them, particularly if they get away with it a couple of times. Such thefts may progress to more serious crimes such as burglary. Unfortunately, this type of criminal behaviour often occurs with teenagers who are relatively un-supervised and who are also unemployed and wish to acquire material goods such as televisions and videos for themselves. Inevitably, in many cases they eventually find themselves in court charged with criminal offences.

Drug addicts may also steal in order to support their habit. Parents should impart to their children a respect for the property of others and be suspicious if a teenager suddenly acquires expensive things for which they cannot possibly have paid. It is, undoubtedly, a temptation if a deprived youngster sees others who have more than they have, but emphasis has to be laid upon the devastating effect that a burglary, for example, can have on the victim. For many people, particularly the elderly, the violation of their home means that they may become virtually house-bound and suffer profound depression. A recent study has shown that child victims of burglary, who have had items stolen which are precious to them and which may have been purchased with considerable financial sacrifice, such as bicycles, suffer quite severe and prolonged psychological distress. Bringing the thieves face to face with their victims may well do more than any amount of legal penalties.

AGGRESSION

Aggression implies that the individual makes blind attacks as a reaction to frustration, but such aggression is not always directed against the immediate cause of the frustration. A teenager who has been subjected to criticism may come home and shout at a sibling, slam the door, or kick the furniture. Sometimes aggression is directed against the self, and particularly disturbed and isolated teenagers may cut themselves, pick constantly at their skin, or pull out lumps of their hair.

Seriously aggressive behaviour may sometimes be the result of living in an atmosphere, for example of marital violence, where aggression is virtually the norm and comes to appear as an answer to every situation. It is a sad fact that many such teenagers, who in realistic moments disapprove of such violence, often find themselves repeating the same pattern of behaviour in their own lives. Parents should try to demonstrate that reasoned argument and discussion is the solution to frustration, rather than physically or verbally attacking others. Aggression is a sign that the teenager has not learnt how to deal with others in a socially acceptable way and its management should be directed towards teaching self-assertion without the necessity for violence.

Aggressive behaviour in a previously normal youngster may

be a sign of alcohol or substance abuse, or of the development of a psychiatric illness.

PROMISCUITY

Indiscriminate, casual contact with a number of partners is a more favoured method of social defiance with girls than boys, who are more likely to steal or be aggressive. Promiscuous behaviour, contrary to the beliefs of some adults, is not a product of an insatiable sexual appetite, but of a desire for closeness and affection. Indeed, many promiscuous girls experience little in the way of sexual satisfaction since, by definition, they frequently have unthinking and uncaring partners. I remember in New York having a patient whose mother was somewhere in the Bahamas with her fourth husband. The girl, a mature-looking 13-year-old, had absconded from her expensive and exclusive boarding school and was found partially naked in a park with a group of soldiers. Her outward attitude was that she could never say 'no' to a request for sex. To me she privately confessed 'I don't like sex. It hurts.'

For teenagers of both sexes who live on the streets, promiscuity becomes a way to eke out a living. Where such behaviour occurs in a more conventional family setting, it illustrates several facts about the teenager. Firstly, her self-esteem is so low that she is prepared to offer herself sexually to anyone who asks, since she sees this as the only way of gaining their approval. Alternatively, she may be wishing to establish herself as someone of importance within her peer group, having been rejected by them. Most importantly, she is seeking the affection and approval from casual encounters which she cannot obtain from her family. Rarely, a teenager may be forced into prostitution by the need to find money for a drug habit. It follows that, with such a profound emotional disturbance, the teenager and the family will require expert counselling. In some cases, which should also be taken seriously, a teenage girl who is in fact a virgin may boast about sexual adventures, often in the most lurid detail, in order to gain attention.

RUNNING AWAY FROM HOME

In a young teenager this is practically always a sign of serious conflict situation and of the adolescent's unhappiness and need for help. Often such a problem has been developing over some time, and parents should endeavour to deal with the causes before there is a serious breach. Many children who leave home are afraid or too proud to return, especially if they feel that nothing will change and they will only be punished. Occasionally, they are led astray by a desire for adventure, but then usually return. More often, they soon find themselves poverty-stricken, sleeping rough and being exploited by others, as well as becoming adept at avoiding apprehension by the police.

Older teenagers may leave home in a fit of pique after an argument about their behaviour. Parents cannot necessarily persuade them to return, but should always ensure that they are in reasonable accommodation and in a position to look after themselves. It often happens that, after the adventure of living in a bedsit wears off, the teenager will be more than happy if they can return home. Parents can often avoid such situations by conducting a dialogue about the limits of behaviour rather than issuing edicts. They should avoid putting the teenager in a situation where the latter's pride forces them to leave. Thus, in a dispute the teenager should be left with an alternative, rather than being told, 'If you do not conform to the rules, you will have to leave home.'

WHAT TO DO IF A TEENAGER IS ACCUSED OF CRIMINAL OFFENCE

- The parents should obtain details of the charge.
- They should attempt to obtain an account of what happened from the police and the teenager.
- They should immediately seek legal advice and, if necessary, apply for legal aid from a lawyer who is sympathetic to, and interested in, the problems of young people.
- They should support their child in any court appearance and make it clear that they will continue to do so. In the case of less serious crime, it is very important that magistrates, when deciding upon sentencing, appreciate that a young offender will have parental supervision.

9

TEENAGERS WITH SPECIAL NEEDS

Adolescence can be a difficult enough time for those with no health or educational problems. Long-standing childhood illnesses or learning difficulties and physical problems that begin in adolescence require special understanding.

Adolescents with a chronic illness have occasion to visit their family doctor regularly and, therefore, it is very important that a mutually good personal relationship should be established. Parents should be prepared to encourage this and, at the same time, respect the confidentiality between the doctor and the young patient. An opportunity must be offered to the teenager to consult the doctor privately, no matter how concerned the parents may be. They should also avoid trying to involve the doctor in any subterfuge, albeit with the best intentions, which will only make the adolescent feel that the medical practitioner, often already perceived by them as an authoritarian figure, is in league with the parents against them. For example, it may be felt by both parents and family doctor that a psychiatric opinion would be valuable. Instead of this possibly unpalatable fact being explained to the teenager, the psychiatrist is produced, like a rabbit out of a hat, as someone who just 'happened to be passing'. It is not to be wondered at that the teenager refuses to talk and storms off in a rage. Parents should try to ensure that the teenager is able to see a doctor who is sensitive to the problems of young people and one to whom the adolescent can relate. Under these circumstances, there should be no difficulty for the doctor in gaining the adolescent's agreement for discussion with the parents when necessary.

DIABETES

The normal adolescent opposition to authority and resistance to external controls can create great difficulties for the young diabetic. The condition may be more easily accepted if diagnosed in early childhood, since a routine of diet and necessary injections will have been established. When diabetes is diagnosed at the time of puberty or later, it can create considerable resentment and anxiety about the future. There is bound to be concern about having children and the possibility of becoming disabled. There may also be an inability to pursue the sort of career that the adolescent had in mind. In some cases, there is a denial of the illness so that the teenager does not keep to a diet or take the correct dosage of insulin. Parents need to be aware of the possibility that, if a meal is missed or too much insulin is taken, there may be a rapid fall in the blood sugar (hypoglycaemia) heralded by sweating, giddiness and feelings of tremulousness which are followed by coma, unless food is taken immediately.

Young diabetics need special support and careful education about their condition and should be helped to realise the importance of diabetic control in enabling them to lead a normal life. They should have a health professional who takes an interest in them and with whom they feel comfortable. Support groups can also be very helpful and beneficial.

Smoking is very detrimental in diabetes because of the blood vessel problems which can be associated with the illness, and should be actively discouraged.

EPILEPSY

The prejudice that still exists in some quarters about this condition can make things very difficult for an adolescent. There are problems about employment and driving. There is embarrassment about uncontrolled fits and a fear of rejection by the peer group. There can be resentment about having to take medication which may have side-effects. In addition, certain forms of epilepsy can lead to rather bizarre behaviour just prior to the onset of a fit or to transient aggression, of which the adolescent is unaware and which is not intentional. Occasionally, the drugs required to control the fits may lead to depression. In addition, there is always the risk of injury during the fit and safeguards have to be taken to prevent this.

It is extremely important that the best professional help

should be obtained in order to exclude any treatable cause of the condition and to institute the most appropriate and least intrusive regime of medication. The family, and particularly the siblings, should be made aware of the nature of an epileptic fit, how it is brought about in the brain, and the simple safety measures, such as inserting something between the teeth, that are required during a fit. Parents also have to strike a balance between appropriate concern and overprotectiveness, which can lead to chronic invalidism. They must be prepared to cope with periods of depression or anxiety which can occur as a response to the condition. It has to be emphasised, however, that the majority of epileptics can have their fits fully controlled by medication and are thus able to lead a fully normal life. Self-help groups run by organisations such as the British Epilepsy Association have a very positive role to play.

DIALYSIS

The need for kidney dialysis implies a serious condition. Unlike the child, who has a very limited perception of death, the adolescent is usually very aware and fearful of their mortality. The need for dialysis curtails normal activities and is a constant reminder that they have a life-threatening illness. At a time when they wish to build up an attractive body image, they are made aware that their physique is not strong like that of their peers. There is also the uncertainty of waiting for a transplant and the fear of its possible rejection. Sometimes, former girl- or boyfriends avoid the teenager because they cannot cope with the stresses of the illness or do not know what to say. There may be a withdrawal from life because of a fear of making emotional commitments and difficulties with career or educational prospects.

The role of the parents is a hard and trying one. Naturally, they are very concerned and fearful about the teenager's future. At the same time they have to try to be optimistic and positive, whilst doing all they can to enable the adolescent to lead as normal a life as possible. They must be prepared to allow the teenager to talk about their fears and to be understanding and sympathetic, whilst at the same time laying emphasis upon the fact that a successful transplant will enable a return to normal living. Contact with those who have already had such transplants can be very encouraging in this respect.

CANCERS AND LEUKAEMIA

The same advice applies to those, fortunately few, adolescents who face painful and prolonged medical treatment for cancers or leukaemia. The side-effects of the drugs used for therapy, such as nausea, vomiting and loss of hair, are very distressing. In addition, there is a possibility of mutilating surgery such as the removal of a limb. Most teenagers cope with this very bravely and channel their suffering into positive fields. However, there is bound to be an initial reaction of shock, fear and anger at the diagnosis and the question, 'why has it happened to me?' There will also be periods of depression, often as a result of treatment, curtailment of activities, and prolonged hospitalisation. At these times, in particular, teenagers look to their parents for support and the latter must be able not only to offer this, but also to cope with the anger and grief that serious illness arouses in the sufferer. Contact with other teenage patients is important because of the supportive camaraderie. In addition, parents who have to come to terms with their own distress will often benefit from relatives' support groups.

ASTHMA

Most adolescents who suffer from asthma have experienced it since childhood. However, the increased awareness and perceptions of puberty make it often a more frightening condition for them at this time. The attacks may cause loss of schooling and a feeling of disability, so that the teenager comes to regard themselves as an invalid who has to be protected. There is often considerable fear occasioned by the difficulty in breathing during the attacks themselves. Parents should pay particular regard to the influence of any emotional factors that provoke an asthma attack and ensure that the teenager is trained in how to use any ventilators of medication prescribed. They should also encourage relaxation techniques, which may obviate the more serious aspects of the asthmatic attack. Again, it is very important to provide as normal a life as possible and not to encourage a retreat into invalidism.

PHYSICAL DISABILITY

Loss of physical capacity, whether due to birth injury, childhood illnesses, or accident is particularly keenly felt at adolescence which is a time for looking critically at the body image. If possible, disfiguring birthmarks or limb deformity should be corrected as soon as possible in childhood. Parents often have to work hard to counter the assumption that severe physical impairment implies mental disability also, as those who saw the film *My Left Foot*, which told the story of Christy Brown, who triumphed over cerebral palsy by writing with his left foot, will appreciate. Teenagers with physical disabilities should be enabled to mix in a normal educational system with their peers and to participate in as many activities as possible. Under certain circumstances, where there are severe sensory deficits in the field of sight and hearing, special educational facilities may have to be arranged.

The abrupt onset of severe paralysis, as in a car or sporting accident, is bound to have a devastating effect upon a teenager. Sometimes there may be profound anger, resentment, and antisocial behaviour. Others initially adopt the role of the 'perfect' invalid, compliant and courageous, only to shatter that image by the development of deep depression. It is not normal for an adolescent to have to face the rest of their life confined to a wheelchair and it requires considerable counselling to enable them to come to terms with this. Whilst parents cannot protect their children from all the hazards of life, they should do their best to prevent accidental injuries by encouraging safety standards in driving cars, riding motor cycles or in sporting activities.

MENTAL HANDICAP

The onset of puberty often brings particular difficulties for the parents of mentally handicapped children. Some at least can be avoided by education in earlier life. Sometimes mentally handicapped girls may be sexually exploited because they do not fully appreciate the consequences of their actions. Minor sexual offences can occur, usually due to a lack of understanding of what is regarded as normal behaviour. Parents have to be specially patient in explaining sexual development and ensuring that those who are vulnerable are protected, without being denied the opportunity to have normal relationships with the opposite sex. Undoubtedly, there are considerable employment problems for the mentally handicapped, but some of these can be obviated by taking as much advantage as possible of educational opportunities and of special training schemes. Mentally handicapped adolescents sometimes have difficulty with job interviews and, because they lack social skills, are shy at expressing themselves or do not dress or behave appropriately. Parents can help them in this regard, and can also ensure that they make the most of their potential. Indeed, all parents, whether or not they have a teenager with special needs, can help such adolescents by educating and encouraging their own teenagers in a sympathetic understanding of mental or physical disabilities in others. The normal adolescent combination of idealism and practicality will often ensure that appropriate help is given without producing an attitude of invalidism.

10

PSYCHIATRIC ILLNESS

DEPRESSION

Depression is the commonest psychiatric problem during the adolescent years. Some mild degree of despondency is natural after a distressing event such as an examination failure, a quarrel with a friend, or an unhappy love affair. However, the healthy teenager will normally recover within a few days and be once more able to plan their future. Whilst parents should be understanding and constructive in dealing with such episodes of low spirits, too much should not be made of them. It is just as easy to encourage a state of prolonged psychological invalidism as it is to produce a physical one. The idea that every slight setback in life has to be the subject of prolonged psychotherapeutic soul searching is only likely to discourage the adolescent from reaching any decisions for themselves. Teenagers are impressionable, and so should not be allowed to believe that every minor change in their mood is of abiding interest. It is preferable to tackle such difficulties in a practical way – deciding about examination resits, suggesting alternative opportunities for making friends, discussing why the job interview went wrong, and so on.

This does not mean, however, that deepening depression should not be taken very seriously indeed. Usually such depression develops in response to an event which has a particular significance for the adolescent and which strikes at the heart of their whole security. The sudden death of a grandparent to whom the child was very close and to whom they have not had a chance to say goodbye, is a case in point. A patient of mine who had suffered severe emotional deprivation as a child had always wanted to take up the nursing of seriously ill children as a way of compensating for her own unhappy upbringing. She was plunged into depression when, shortly after being accepted for nursing training, a back injury robbed her of both her job prospects and her possible home.

Suicidal attempts have, unfortunately, become increasingly common in adolescents, and are sometimes successful. In most cases they are an appeal for help or an attempt at escape from what seems to be an intolerable situation. It is also an unfortunate fact that the wide availability of prescribed or over-the-counter medication has led to the idea that such medication is comparatively harmless. This is not the case. A number of medicaments can have prolonged and possibly lethal effects if taken in quantity and parents should make their children aware of this fact. Moreover, they should encourage their children to cope with problems without recourse to drugs.

In many teenagers an attempt at suicide is a reaction to stress and often has ambivalent motives. A girl whose boyfriend has given her up for another may wish to win him back by making him feel sorry for her and, at the same time, be venting her anger by thinking how guilty he will be when he realises she has died. In fantasy, she sees herself as not being really dead, but able to witness his remorse and grief. In such cases there are frequently indications that the adolescent is feeling desperate. They often visit their doctor complaining of depression, talk of suicide to their friends, or threaten those who have upset them with the idea that they will end it all. Such threats always have to be taken seriously, since they indicate that the teenager is in a situation with which they cannot cope and are liable to act impulsively and irrationally. Often suicide attempts are made in circumstances where the adolescent can reasonably expect to be discovered and they may, after ingesting tablets, almost immediately announce the fact. Unfortunately, sometimes there is a miscalculation and the overdose is more serious than was intended. If the adolescent seems to be increasingly depressed, every effort should be made to help them to talk about their problems and, if necessary, enlist the advice and support of a counsellor skilled in dealing with such difficulties. Any medication that parents are taking should be locked away, since distressed teenagers may act impulsively by swallowing handfuls of assorted tablets which have more deleterious effects than they anticipated.

Any suicide attempt should be taken seriously, but those which the teenager might obviously expect to be lethal, such as an attempt at hanging, jumping from high buildings, stabbing the body in vital areas, and so on, are most often those which are likely to be repeated and should be the subject for psychiatric intervention. Such attempts often occur when the teenager feels in a trapped and friendless situation – in prison, in some environment where they are being seriously bullied or ill-treated, or where they have become completely estranged from any family or peer group support.

In a minority of teenagers, depression may come out of the blue without there being any obvious stress. Under these circumstances, parents should give serious consideration to the possibility of physical illness or to drug or alcohol abuse. If these are excluded, this may well be the type of depression which responds to anti-depressant drug therapy. Anti-depressants are medications used for the specific treatment of severe depression. They are not tranquillisers, are not habit-forming, and are only taken for the duration of the depression. However, the majority of cases of depression in teenagers will respond to counselling and do not require medication.

Warning signs that a depression is becoming severe are:

• increased and persistent gloominess of mood which is not altered by what would normally be pleasant and distracting events
• loss of appetite and weight
• disturbed sleep pattern. Normally adolescents sleep very well, but in depression there may be difficulty in getting off to sleep and/or wakening in the early hours of the morning
• talk about suicide or expression of ideas that life is not worth living
• when the teenager has ideas that they are unworthy or are to blame for their condition
• inability to concentrate and a decline in school or work performance
• neglect of personal appearance and hygiene.

Any teenager who is admitted to hospital after a suicide attempt is medically assessed and appropriate treatment will be advised. However, the ideal would be to prevent such attempts in the first place and, whilst this may not always be possible, parents should pay particular attention to early warning signs and, if they cannot cope with the problems themselves, seek advice. This does not necessarily have to be medical. There are a number of agencies, listed at the end of this book, who offer therapy and support to depressed young people.

A number of principles need to be pointed out. The teenager should never be made to feel that their problems are unimportant or that their family do not care. Whilst some of their situations may not necessarily offer easy solutions, what the majority of adolescents are looking for is a person in whom they can confide. A difficulty which seems trivial to an adult may be of profound significance to a teenager, and depressive and suicidal ideas are greatly worsened if there seems to be no escape route. Thus, if an adolescent seems bitterly unhappy in school, residential work, or any other situation from which the parents are able to remove them, then they should do so. Someone who is depressed should never be told to 'pull themselves together'. Being depressed already inclines the sufferer to self-blame and such remarks only make a depressed person feel worse, because they imagine others think they are not trying. Depressed teenagers are particularly sensitive to critical remarks about their appearance or achievements and such comments may be the final straw which precipitates a suicide attempt. Relatives, and siblings in particular, should be encouraged to be understanding and positive. Often those who are depressed feel they will never get better and they need to be constantly reassured that this is not the case.

SCHIZOPHRENIA

Schizophrenia is a serious mental illness that normally begins between the ages of 18 to 25, but can commence in the early teens. There are many misconceptions about this condition and any deviation from normal teenage behaviour should not be taken as indicating that this illness is developing. Moreover, many of the symptoms can be mimicked by abuse of drugs, particularly cannabis, speed, or LSD.

The early signs of a possible schizophrenic illness in a young person could be the following:

- *Gradual withdrawal from society and friends* The adolescent begins to spend longer periods in their room, in itself a normal part of adolescent behaviour. However, in the case of someone developing schizophrenia this is frequently accompanied by complete inactivity. The teenager lies in bed, preoccupied with their own thoughts. They have no contact with previous friends and often there is a reversal of sleep pattern, so that the adolescent sleeps all day and is awake, often wandering around the house or around the streets, all night.
- *Decline in performance* One of the symptoms of schizophrenia is difficulty in thinking, so there is a problem with concentration. A previously clever adolescent may show a

progressive deterioration in their intellectual capacity. It becomes hard for them to do serious studying and prepare for examinations; their school marks will become poorer and observant teachers will have noticed that they have become dreamy, withdrawn or indifferent, lacking their usual spontaneity. Someone who is at work may be unable to get up in the mornings in order to get there on time or lose jobs because of bad time-keeping, slowness or poor work performance.

- *A change in emotional responses* The adolescent may be even more than usually moody. They may have bouts of depression or, alternatively, moods of excitement and agitation for no apparent reason. On other occasions, the mood may be one of apathy and indifference. Normally, adolescence is a time of rapid emotional change, but parents should be concerned if there are prolonged and unexplained changes of mood.

- *An excessive preoccupation with physical appearance* Again, it is natural for teenagers to worry a good deal about how they look and about minor physical imperfections. However, at the onset of schizophrenia there may be what can only be regarded as an abnormal involvement with one particular aspect of the appearance which, in reality, is quite normal. The adolescent may constantly go to the doctor asking for plastic surgery on a perfectly acceptable nose, for example, or stand for hours in front of the mirror, examining a minute pimple or tiny skin blemish. This may progress to expressions that the appearance has become altered in some way by external forces. A girl may say, for example, that one of her rivals is putting noxious substances into her face cream to make her look ugly.

- *Prolonged depression* Whilst sadness and feeling low in spirits is quite common for short periods in adolescence, such depression usually responds fairly promptly to environmental changes, counselling, or anti-depressant medication. In developing schizophrenia, the depression may not respond to such measures so readily and seems to be a response to the illness itself rather than a reaction to real life stresses. There is tiredness, inertia, loss of interest, poor appetite and withdrawal. These symptoms may lead to the adolescent becoming involved with drugs such as amphetamines, which initially give them energy, but can subsequently precipitate more obvious schizophrenic symptoms.

- *Strange ideas and behaviour* One of the most distressing symptoms of schizophrenia is a distortion of reality. The adolescent may begin to believe that people are spying on them, that their food is being poisoned or that messages are being sent to them, indicating that they are to leave on some special mission. Many normal teenagers become preoccupied with philosophical and metaphysical issues, but in schizophrenia the thoughts become increasingly incoherent, so that others have extreme difficulty in following the line of argument. The beliefs may cause the adolescent to abruptly leave home in pursuit of their supposed mission, to insist on preparing all their own food, or searching their rooms in the hope of finding devices that they believe have been put there in order to overhear their conversations.

- *Anti-social activities* The strange ideas that can occur in schizophrenia may lead to a previously stable teenager becoming involved in trouble. They may be found wandering to escape from supposed persecutors, become angry with others because they imagine that they are being talked about, or exhibit disturbed behaviour under the influence of drugs.

- *Loss of contact with reality* so that the teenager is unable to accept that they are ill in any way. This may pose a problem for parents in that the adolescent may be resistant to the idea of any investigation. However, there is usually a time when they become willing to accept medical intervention, if the parents are patient and explain their concern.

It cannot be emphasised too strongly that any of the above symptoms may be of no extraordinary significance in itself. A diagnosis of schizophrenia is made by a psychiatrist only after a period of careful observation and investigation of every factor involved. Many of the symptoms described may only be a transient feature of teenage development or a sign of some other disturbance. However, if parents are concerned they should seek professional advice immediately. They should remember that schizophrenia, although a serious psychiatric illness, can be treated and that it is to the teenager's advantage that such therapy should commence as soon as possible. Moreover, if there has been any indication of any schizophrenic-like symptoms, they should be particularly emphatic in warning the adolescent about the dangers of illicit drugs.

11

FACING TERMINAL ILLNESS AND DEATH

In the past many teenagers died from illnesses such as tuberculosis which are now preventable and treatable. As can be
seen from the gravestones in old churchyards, childbirth caused
the death of a number of teenage girls. Fortunately, nowadays
death is rare amongst adolescents, but the most common
causes are cancer, suicide or violent death, as in road traffic
accidents.

The death of a loved one is always extremely hard to accept
and such acceptance is even more difficult when the person
who has died, or is dying, is young, with a life which had
seemed full of promise. An adolescent faced with the diagnosis
of a life-threatening illness will be frightened of what the future
holds, how the disease will affect them mentally and physically,
the way it will change their life, the effects of the treatment,
and, of course, the possibility of death. There will also be anger
and the questioning, 'Why has it happened to me?' Added to
this, there may be an irrational guilt that some misdemeanour
has brought the illness about. Parents have to be prepared to
deal with all these emotions and may need help in doing so.
The siblings will be affected by the disruption of home life, their
own ignorance about the illness, and their guilt about being
healthy. They may feel left out of any discussion, be concerned
at their parents' distressed mental state, and be unsure about
what to tell their friends. Siblings in the adolescent group often
have a strong wish to be included in discussions about what is
wrong with their brother or sister, what is going to happen to
them, and how they can be helpful and supportive.

Many life-threatening illnesses are cured these days, although
there are often stressful treatments to be undergone. However,
in a minority of adolescents therapy proves incapable of

altering the disease process and death becomes inevitable. In my view, parents and doctors should be as honest as possible with the adolescent and the rest of the family throughout the illness. What is going to happen has to be taken stage by stage, since it is impossible for anyone to forecast how a disease will progress or how quickly death can be expected. If at all possible, the parents should be first to tell the adolescent any bad news. How much they reveal must obviously be a matter for them, dependent on their knowledge of the child, how they will react, and what questions they ask. They should always try to leave hope, if at all possible, and should ask themselves whether the adolescent wants to know the whole truth or whether it should be allowed to emerge gradually. However, it should be borne in mind that coping with dying is often made more difficult by the strategies that are frequently employed by all those involved. There is an unspoken agreement to avoid discussing the truth in the belief that this will be less painful. But, as the patient becomes weaker, it becomes obvious to them that they are not improving and it can be a source of relief to be able to discuss the future realistically with those they love and trust, without relying upon subterfuges.

Parents can also expect the doctors and nurses to offer them support at this very difficult time. There is no doubt that a number of those caring for a young person whose death is approaching find this exceedingly hard to accept and to face. However, much more emphasis is now being placed upon the importance of counselling for the dying patient and so parents should find they can work with the professionals caring for the adolescent to minimise their child's distress as much as possible.

Adolescents faced with death may react in a variety of ways and it is important that parents are able to unconditionally accept their reactions, including the anger and sadness which they must inevitably feel. A minority of teenagers will react with intense depression and withdrawal. There may be intellec-tualisation, where the adolescent tries to learn as much as possible about the illness. Others may adopt an attitude of cheerful denial and so remain optimistic almost until the end. There may be a frantic effort to cram a lifetime's experience into a few months and sometimes a search for relief in alcohol or sexual activity. Some triumph completely over their illness by trying to leave a memorial behind them, either in the form of collecting for charities to help those suffering like themselves or by exposing their feeling about dying in art, words or music. Parents may find that a holiday or an expedition which the teenager has always desired will give the whole family the chance to be together and be a source of happy memories.

Parents also have to cope with their own grief, shock, anger and depression, which are all normal emotions when the death of a child becomes inevitable. Moreover, they have to think about the other siblings. Brothers and sisters have to be given the opportunity to understand what is really happening in words that they can comprehend and in a way which is relevant to their age. They should not be told untruths such as 'John is going to hospital to have a little operation and then he will be all right', if it is obvious that the future is uncertain and the operation is a serious one, such as the amputation of a leg or an operation for a brain tumour. Siblings also need time to make their peace with the teenager who is dying and they cannot do this if they do not realise the full facts. Parents should not be afraid to share their grief with their other children, but should, at the same time, try to adopt as positive an attitude as possible to the remaining time that the dying teenager has to live. Most importantly, they should share their grief with each other and not allow it to break up their marriage. A surprising number of marriages do end in divorce after the death of a child. There may be a number of reasons for this. In some cases the parents react in quite different ways to their loss and so do not communicate. The father may be expected, by society and his family, to be strong and not to show his grief, which then leads to depression and inability to cope. The parents may be unable to accept their loss and so blame each other.

It is essential for everyone at their moment of death to have privacy, quiet, familiar surroundings, and the love of relatives. If it is at all possible, adolescents should be able to die at home. Sometimes the individual who is dying may feel that they should be in hospital to save the family distress. The family may also be fearful of how they will be able to cope, but such fears can be obviated by the skilled care given by Macmillan nurses and by help from the hospice movement. After death, I believe it is important for everyone to see the body and to attend the funeral, including all the siblings. Grief is a natural and prolonged process and cannot be got over in a few days or weeks. In order for death to be fully accepted, there has to be a realisation that the dead person is not going to return and the funeral ceremony acts as a marker that this is the case. This is well illustrated by the prolonged and unresolved grief, often lasting for many years, of parents whose children have disappeared and who have no identifiable body over which they can mourn.

After an adolescent has died, it is important to talk about

them, to dwell upon the happy times, and to set them in the memory as a real person with their individual merits, faults and foibles. If the dead person is never mentioned, siblings, in particular, will conclude that they have been forgotten and will be afraid to talk of their grief. It is natural that parents should wish to always remember their child, but they should not build a shrine which never lets them come to terms with their grief. Many parents may feel that their child is best commemorated by the giving of some prize or gift to a school or other institution which will benefit teenagers. It is important, too, that grief should not be dulled by tranquillisers or alcohol, tempting though this may be, since it only leads to long-term problems. It is much more valuable to talk to others, possibly within the family or to outside counsellors, about all the feelings which bereavement unleashes. Parents should not be afraid to express their grief to each other. They should talk of the dead teenager with love, but should be careful not to deify them in the sense of comparing other siblings unfavourably to them. Nothing can be more soul-destroying than to be brought up in the shadow of a dead person with whom one can never hope to compete in the eyes of one's parents.

At least where death is expected, there is a time for preparation and an opportunity for everyone concerned to say farewell to the dying person. Suicide or a violent death, as in a car accident, will come as a devastating blow. There will inevitably be self-blame: 'Why did I not recognise the depression?' 'Why did I give him that motorbike?' There may also be reproach between the parents and very considerable anger if the teenager has been the innocent victim of a drunken or reckless driver who subsequently appears to have been inadequately punished. Parents and siblings may live and relive the adolescent's last moments, wondering if they suffered, whether they realised that they were dying and so on.

As previously mentioned, matters are made even worse if no body has been found and the parents do not know whether the teenager is alive or dead. Grief about any violent death will often take longer to resolve and will be complicated by thoughts of what could or should have been said or done prior to the suicide or accident. Blame may be attached to those considered responsible and may lead to fantasies or actual acts of aggression against them. Expert and sympathetic counselling may often be needed, but parents should try to avoid the bereavement causing a rift between them or the other grieving members of the family. To try to prevent such tragedies, it is important that families should be acutely aware of how depression can affect a vulnerable teenager, of the possibility of a suicide attempt, and should always be prepared to offer support and help. Moreover, they should discourage the idea that reckless speeding and taking risks on the road is a sign of anything other than crass stupidity and selfishness, and should set an example themselves in this regard. In resolving grief after a fatality, either by suicide or accident, the parents have to come to an acceptance that the incident was unforeseen, that they did their best, and, most difficult of all, to try to forgive those whom they regard as responsible.

It must be emphasised that grieving is a prolonged process. In the early days after bereavement, the parents may have fantasies that the teenager is still alive and dreams in which they recover from the illness or accident. There may also be irrational anger against doctors who could not keep them alive or against other parents who have healthy children. Sometimes, the bereaved person may imagine that they see or hear the dead child and fear they are going mad. Things can be made worse if neighbours or friends avoid them because they do not know what to say. Under these circumstances, parents should make it clear that they wish to talk about the teenager and should not be afraid to express their sense of loss. Often they can derive considerable support from talking with other parents who have been bereaved. They also have to try to be understanding about the reactions of others. For any normal parents, the possible loss of their children is something that can be too distressing to contemplate. It is, therefore, not surprising that some of them cannot easily talk to a parent who has had that experience and are at a loss as to how to help or sympathise.

Depression is a natural sequence to bereavement, particularly where there has been a violent death. It can be helped by dwelling upon the happy times with the teenager and by thinking of all the good things that came from their life. Siblings may also experience problems such as anxiety about illness or death, fears about going to school, or, in younger children, clinging and regressive behaviour. This will pass if they are able to express their grief and, at the same time, appreciate that, while the dead brother or sister was deeply loved, they, the living, have an equal and vital place in their parents' affections. The natural resolution of grief is an acceptance of the loss and the ability to remember the teenager in a happy way rather than with sadness. However, it is not unexpected to find that, after months or even years, a sudden incident will temporarily bring back the grief for a short period of time. This too is quite normal and can be alleviated by talking to someone close about it. It should not be forgotten, also, that grandparents, and other relations who have been particularly close to the teenager, will grieve and have need for comfort and support.

12

THE OUTSIDE WORLD

LEAVING HOME

Leaving home to go on a course of higher education or under-take other training can be an exciting and, at the same time, an emotionally exacting experience. There is separation from parental support, from peer group friends, from the rela-tively settled world of school and completely new horizons amongst strangers to be faced.

Fortunately, most teenagers make the adjustment fairly quickly, although the majority experience some degree of homesickness. The outgoing telephone lines from university halls of residence are always in great demand during this period. If possible, it is probably wise for parents to be available to offer support and guidance on the telephone over this transitional period, particularly where a teenager has rarely been away from home for any prolonged period previously.

It is natural that parents should miss the adolescent, par-ticularly if they are the last of the family to leave home. If there are problems within the marriage, this sadness at separation can be more marked and a number of partners realise that they have ceased to have any meaningful contact with each other, apart from bringing up their children. However, even in cases where the relationship is a close one mothers, in particular, may experience a sense of loss in the initial period when a teenager leaves home. It takes a little time to adjust to the fact that there is now no one dependent upon them. These feelings are con-siderably alleviated if the parents have outside interests which they can look forward to continuing together and if both have what they see as worthwhile aims for their future life.

The excitement of a fresh environment and the companion-ship of other individuals who are in a similar situation soon helps most teenagers to begin a new and more adult life. Things may be more difficult for the shy, socially isolated adolescent at this time and it may well be better for them to go to a smaller university or polytechnic rather than an overwhelmingly large one. It is also wise for all prospective university or polytechnic students to have given careful consideration to the course they really *want* to take, rather than seizing the first one they are offered. The drop-out rate at the end of the first term is quite considerable, because students are unhappy and realise they have made a mistake in their choice of course.

From the early teens onwards parents should have been encouraging an increasing degree of independence on the part of the adolescent. It is tempting, if the parent is lonely or unhappy, to try to place the child in the psychological position of a surrogate partner, but this temptation should be avoided since it can only lead to what can be a crippling dependency. Some anxieties about a new venture are natural, but they should not be fostered by expressions of overconcern from the parents, who should view the teenager leaving home as a step on the way to adult life. However, they do not need to go to the opposite extreme as in the case of one student who was rarely able to go home for his holidays because his room had been let out to a lodger. Adolescents still want to have a secure, familiar base to which they can return.

LEARNING TO LIVE WITH OTHERS

This can be particularly trying for the rather nervous and self-conscious teenager and for those who have been used to a considerable degree of privacy at home. Some adjustments can be made easier by using the earlier years to encourage activities outside the home environment, where the adolescent has to co-operate with others and consider their feelings. They should also be helped to become sufficiently self-assertive to ensure that others do not take undue advantage of them. Sharing is good, but it should be sharing on an equal basis, so that vulnerable teenagers do not find themselves deprived of cherished possessions or have expensive textbooks constantly borrowed by others and never returned. On the other hand, part of the camaraderie of college is the ability to help others out if they really need it.

COPING WITH A FREER ENVIRONMENT

The first few months away from home may lead to an intensification of pre-existing psychological problems or the emergence of new ones, most commonly depression and anxiety. There is a need to adjust to a more adult way of life, to meet many new people, to take responsibility for independent study, and to take decisions about matters for which there may previously have been reliance upon parents.

For example, teenagers find themselves in a much freer sexual environment, with all its implications. They are mixing with others about whose background they know little and may be rendered more vulnerable if they feel lonely or homesick. Consequently, depression may result from an unhappy love affair or there may be anxiety about how far they should go in a relationship. Universities and colleges have counselling services which specialise in helping students to deal with such emotional problems, but it may be that the teenager will prefer to talk about these matters to their parents or siblings.

Good sixth forms at school or college will have already encouraged individual responsibility for learning and study. However, many students find the change from the established routine of school to the greater freedom and anonymity of a large university a bewildering one. They have to ensure that they get up to go to lectures and tutorials, and often examinations seem a long way in the distance. Whilst one does not want to deprive them of all the enjoyment and fun of student life, it is wise that they have a regular plan of study from the beginning, so that at the end of term they do not find themselves confronted with a vast amount of uncompleted work. All students are allocated their own personal tutor who will give them practical advice about their courses and discuss any difficulties that they are having. If the student feels that they have embarked upon the wrong course, they should take immediate steps to try to change to a more appropriate one. However, they should not accept a course in the hope that they will be able to change to one of the oversubscribed ones such as medicine, veterinary science or law since, under normal circumstances, this will prove impossible.

MANAGING ON A GRANT

Many students find themselves in debt during their training. This has become increasingly the case because the student grant has not kept up with the cost of living and because, for a number of courses, the cost of textbooks is very high. Moreover, whilst for a period they can live in a hall of residence, they then have to move out into more costly lodgings or other accommodation. Whilst some students manage to supplement their grant by vacation jobs, in some fields of study the volume of work and shorter holidays preclude this. Parents can help by ensuring that the teenager knows how to budget and does not rush out to spend all their money in the first week of term, tempting though this might be. The adolescent should leave home equipped to cook at least simple meals and with realistic expectations of what they can afford. Moreover, the parents have to be prepared, if the student is receiving a grant, to supplement this at a modest level if at all possible. Teenagers undertaking higher levels of study should be discouraged from taking out large loans or acquiring numerous credit cards, which may appear a painless way of purchase until the bill, plus the interest, arrives. At this time, the student may feel resentment that they cannot afford the consumer items that contemporaries who are at work can. However, most of them are able to appreciate the long-term benefits of further study in the possibility of more interesting work and greater flexibility and freedom.

FINDING A JOB

It is important that teenagers should prepare themselves for work by obtaining as many qualifications as possible. They and their parents should give considerable thought to the type of work which they are interested in and of which they are capable. It is wise also to show foresight, in the sense of not immediately accepting a job which seems ostensibly the most attractive. For example, work which is less well paid initially, but which offers good training facilities and promotion, is probably better than work which offers higher pay but no future prospects. Teenagers may decide that they wish to change jobs if they find that they would be happier in another type of work, but they should ensure that they have another position before they leave their present one. It is always easier to move from one employment to another rather than from being unemployed. Indeed, long periods of unemployment have a very deleterious effect upon teenagers. They feel they have no position in society, that they have little future, and are not taken seriously by anyone. This can lead to depression and ideas of hopelessness, to indulgence in alcohol and drugs or to anti-social activities to obtain the consumer goods that their peers possess.

Therefore, every effort should be made to ensure that the teenager can obtain work. Sometimes the adolescent lacks motivation or interest and this may date back to scholastic failures in the past. They may be preoccupied with other things and this is particularly so in the case of those who are on drugs or suffering from a psychiatric illness. The parents may have unrealistic expectations, as in the case of intellectual professionals who cannot accept that their children are more suited to and happier working with their hands. Neither should parents encourage the idea that, because a job is not very well paid, it is not worth doing and that the teenagers are being exploited. It may well be that they are getting valuable training and, once they have had some work experience, they can move on to a more interesting, better paid position. The work ethic has become more popular in recent years, and indeed most adolescents and adults are happier when they feel they are contributing something positive to society, when they are able to mix with others in a work situation, and when they are able to save for the things they want in life, not necessarily just material things.

COPING WITH INTERVIEWS

Interviews can be very difficult for many adolescents who lack self-confidence and who are prone to becoming inarticulate, no matter how much they pretend to be sure of themselves. Anxiety at interviews can be lessened by preparation beforehand. It is amazing how many individuals appear at an interview without having given even rudimentary thought to what they might be asked. It is not impressive if, having stated that you are madly interested in the job, you can give no reason why or, having expressed an interest in a topic, it is obvious that you know nothing about it, have not read any books on the subject, and so on. This applies equally to university or polytechnic interviews as it does to job interviews. The candidate should be clear why they want the position, why they are interested in this particular subject, and what their future plans are. They should also be prepared to talk about their hobbies and about any special experience they have had which makes them especially qualified. They should also be ready to undertake any practical tests if these are likely to be required, such as shorthand and typing skills.

PROBLEMS AT WORK

It is not always easy for teenagers to accept the discipline that being at work involves. Often naturally rebellious against authority, they may feel that they are being picked on or criticised unfairly. Shy adolescents may be teased by their fellow workers or there may be sexual harassment by older workers. The teenager has to be encouraged to look at the situation in perspective. If they are sure that they are being treated unfairly, they should approach their boss and discuss the matter in a rational and courteous way. They have to face the fact that they will encounter a number of situations in their life when they have to cope with dictatorial and unpleasant people. On the other hand, it may well be that the discipline about which they complain is designed to benefit everyone and it is they that are in the wrong. Teasing can often be lessened by showing that it is ineffective or by proving to the teasers that the adolescent can do the job as well, if not better, than they can. Similarly, with sexual harassment one has to make a distinction between the office or factory Romeo who is relatively harmless (unfortunately women will always have to suffer unwanted attentions) and the boss who makes it clear that the only way to survive in a job is to give way to his demands. Where there is upsetting sexual harassment or indeed bullying of any kind, the teenager should not hesitate to take advantage of the appropriate complaints procedure. In the end, it may be necessary for them to leave an uncongenial place to find a more pleasant working atmosphere.

ACCEPTING THE TEENAGER'S BOY- OR GIRLFRIEND

Many parents have an ideal partner that they would like their teenager to bring home. Sometimes these expectations are fulfilled and everyone is happy, although it has to be borne in mind that the 'perfect' mate may not turn out to be that in reality. Because of this, parents should be especially cautious about pushing together two young people whom they feel to be ideally suited. They should remember that the choice of partner belongs entirely to the adolescent and that someone who seems to them to be unsuitable may turn out to be just what the teenager needs in terms of support and affection. They should be accepting, non-critical, and, difficult as it may sometimes be, should acknowledge that the teenager has to lead their own independent life and sometimes make their own mistakes in relationships.

THE RESOLUTION OF ADOLESCENCE

Ideally adolescence will end with:

- the attainment of separation and independence from parents and a return to them in an adult relationship of equality
- the establishment of sexual and emotional identity
- the development of a capacity for loving and lasting relationships with members of their peer group
- a commitment to work and an enjoyment of social activities
- the development of a personal moral value system which is based, not upon standards imposed by the parents, but on ideas that the adolescent has thought out for themselves.

Such resolution is usually based, at least partially, upon an observation of parental behaviour. It is thus made more difficult if there is a poor parental example or none at all. Conflict often arises, too, when there is a considerable clash between parental values and the pressures of society around the teenager. This is particularly marked, for example, in some immigrant families where the religious and social values of parents, in issues such as arranged marriages, are in conflict with the freedom of choice that the adolescent sees amongst their peer group.

13

TEENAGERS IN HISTORY

It is only during this century that the concept of adolescence as being a distinct life period has come to be recognised and, even then, only in Western society. In earlier ages it was considered that the onset of puberty marked the transition from childhood to being an adult and the child was then expected to behave accordingly. Some societies still mark this important change by initiation ceremonies attended by village or tribal groups. Such ceremonies are intended to reinforce the young person's allegiance to the particular mores of their society and often involve a degree of cruelty. One of the most barbaric practices, that still involves many girls, is female circumcision, where at any age prior to puberty the more sensitive parts of the female genitalia are cut away, often under unhygienic conditions with no anaesthetic. This is intended to ensure fidelity by abolishing any pleasurable sensation for the female in a sexual relationship. It often results in mutilation, sepsis and scarring which impedes normal childbirth.

History reveals that for many teenagers life was not happy. For the wealthy, marriages were arranged and consummated as soon as puberty was reached, often for the sake of land and family alliances with scant regard for the feelings of the young people. Daughters, in particular, were used as a marriageable commodity to gain more wealth or to bolster up shaky treaties. A powerful man would sometimes not hesitate to murder a rival's young family to rid himself of any possible challengers. Sons were expected to join their fathers in whatever wars they wished to wage and to be wounded or killed in dubious causes. They were often sent from their homes at an early age to live with strangers. In the poorer classes, teenagers were wage slaves, toiling endlessly for little reward and bearing children to do the same. Even less fortunate conquered peoples had their youngsters taken as slaves. Girls were frequently seen as mere sexual objects for the person who owned them. Where a whole group of people endured life of a brutish and short nature, children and teenagers suffered from starvation, disease, and deformity. In some countries young adolescents were deliberately maimed to facilitate begging.

The words of such children were unrecorded, if indeed they were able to articulate them. However, if one wishes to realise what life was like for a well-to-do teenager in the sixteenth century, one can think of poor Lady Jane Grey, the nine day queen, married off in an attempt to gain her relations the throne and beheaded at the age of 16, moving all by her brave bearing at the scaffold. Sir Thomas More, executed by Henry VIII for his religious opinions, was noted for his love for his daughter Margaret and for the fine education he gave her, an attitude very unusual in his day.

The industrial revolution brought a great demand for the labour of young people who worked for long hours in dreadful conditions. Contemporary accounts describe women, children and adolescents in the mines chained, belted, harnessed like dogs, more than half naked. Women would have to work in an advanced state of pregnancy. The lot of servants was little better. They were often regarded as possessions by the master of the house, seduced and then turned out to face the rigours of the workhouse when pregnant. It is not surprising that many teenage girls found their way on to the streets and a short, brutal life of prostitution. The spread of venereal disease in Victorian Britain made virgins a prize commodity, and many young teenagers were sold to brothel keepers. It was not until 1886 that the age of consent for sexual intercourse was raised to 16. The journalist W.T. Stead had, with the co-operation of the Salvation Army which was then, as now, concerned with the welfare of young people, deliberately purchased a child without its father's consent. He publicised this, to show how easily it could be achieved, and was imprisoned, but succeeded in changing the law.

Teenagers often sought refuge in alcohol, which was available quite freely then, and a number were hopeless inebriates by their late teens. Moreover, infectious diseases, particularly tuberculosis, had a particular predilection for adolescents and were responsible for many premature deaths. Again, the children of wealthy parents often fared little better. Sent away to boarding school at an early age, they were frequently subjected to bullying, cruelty and neglect as Dickens described in his portrait of the infamous Dotheboys Hall of Nicholas Nickleby.

The work of philanthrophists like Lord Shaftesbury and of writers such as Dickens helped to ameliorate the material conditions of young people. The psychoanalysts increased the understanding of their inner life. Freud and his contemporaries showed that, for example, sexuality did not suddenly begin at puberty but was present in the young child in its conflicting love and hate relationship with the parents. Moreover, they deduced that, if such relationships were not satisfactorily resolved, they could produce problems later in life. One of their most interesting studies was the demonstration of how the sexual repression current in Viennese society at that time for young women led to psychiatric illness. Sexual conflict often led to so-called hysterical symptoms – a paralysis of a limb or a loss of the voice in the absence of any physical cause. For instance, a teenage girl might seek refuge from a sexuality which was desired, but also feared because of inhibitions in her upbringing, by becoming an invalid. It is noteworthy that such 'hysterical' symptoms, so common in Victorian times, are uncommon now and only tend to occur in groups where having a physical symptom is more acceptable than expressing a psychological difficulty.

Teenagers have always been at risk in times of war. A study of the war graves of the 1914–18 war will reveal how many of those killed were under the age of 20. Their idealism has sometimes been perverted into anti-social activities as it was with the Hitler Youth or the Chinese Red Guard. However, they have more frequently been victims. The diary of Anne Frank reveals how many teenagers, amongst thousands of others, were sent to the gas chambers because of an obscene racial policy. In many countries, large numbers of adolescents still remain underprivileged because of racial, religious or political differences.

Sexuality has, until recent times, been denied to adolescents. Masturbation or 'self-abuse' as it was called in Victorian times, was regarded as harmful and, in extreme cases, the cause of severe mental illness. Many punishments were devised for teenagers found indulging in this quite normal activity. Homosexuality was a crime until the late 60s and those with such an inclination were advised to marry, usually with predictably disastrous consequences. The reaction to a teenager becoming pregnant was to blame the girl, culminating in the policy of making her keep her child, destined for adoption, for a sufficient time to make her aware of her transgression against conventional morality. Many such girls cried for their lost baby for the rest of their lives, even when they married and had another family. Tess of the D'Urbervilles in Hardy's novel of that name is seduced as a teenager and then abandoned, but her love for her baby and grief over its death is compounded by the religious dogma decreeing that, because the child was illegitimate, it could not be buried in consecrated ground.

Today it is accepted in our society that adolescents have become a new class with their own dress, language and music and their own problems and emotional difficulties. The wide range of choices open to them is, in itself, a source of problems. Many feel they lack a set place in society, which may account for their adherence to various cult groups. However, it is perhaps easy to forget that these teenagers, about whom this book has largely been written, are in a minority. In many countries adolescents are still exploited sexually and in work situations, and their lives lack the freedom and enjoyment attained by many teenagers in the West. Rightly, we feel appalled by this, but perhaps we should also reflect that, in our country, adolescents are being sexually abused by those who should care for them, that some from overseas live in a completely servile state terrorised by employers, and that several thousand are forced to sleep on the streets because they are homeless.

14

TEENAGERS IN LITERATURE

Until the nineteenth century, children and teenagers were not taken seriously as subjects for novels and plays. This was, at least partly, because they were regarded as being like little adults with identical, if rather infantile, emotions and attitudes to the world. Romeo and Juliet, although young adolescents, were already embroiled in the power struggle between their two families, a conflict which made their love 'star-crossed'. Their story is perhaps an illustration of how suicide attempts can go gravely wrong. Juliet is given a potion which renders her insensible so that her family believe her dead, as does Romeo when he sees her. Distraught with grief he kills himself, only to have Juliet awaken, as indeed it was intended she should, and end her life when she realises her lover is dead. Shakespeare, for all his great insight into human nature, never had a child protagonist in his plays, although boy actors were common in his day to play female roles. Hamlet, the most adolescent-like of his heroes in his moodiness and rebellion, is perhaps a little older and indeed has been played by some actors of quite mature years. It is of interest, however, that Shakespeare predated Freud in his analysis of Hamlet's overinvolvement with his mother, the sexual jealousy aroused by his stepfather's relationship with her, and all his insecurity and searching, characteristic of teenage years.

The Romantic movement altered the concept held by previous generations that the child was basically full of original sin which had to be corrected. English Romantics, such as Blake and Wordsworth, saw the child as a symbol of human intuitive joy, innocent and in communion with nature until made evil by the adult world. Many nineteenth-century writers had child heroes or heroines, but it is significant that the teenage years were often hastily passed over. For example, Jane Eyre's first ten years of life are described by Charlotte Brontë in great detail, but from then until the age of 18, her life is dealt with in about one paragraph. The observations of the inner world of children do become more acute as the century progresses and culminate in one of the lesser-known works of the American novelist Henry James, *What Maisie Knew*. Maisie is a child caught up in a world of divorce and intense sexual intrigue. Events are seen through her innocent eyes and interpreted by her, whilst the reader is well aware of the adult view. At the end, when Maisie decides to leave with her governess rather than with any of her parents or step-parents who have vied for her attentions for their own selfish reasons, we are left to draw our own conclusions as to what it is about life and human relationships that she has finally found out. Not all the children are paragons either. The Artful Dodger, Tom Sawyer and Huckleberry Finn are all normal and naughty boys in their own way. The girls, on the whole, tend to be more docile, in conformity with Victorian morality.

However, we do have some nineteenth-century studies of adolescents such as the story of Cathy and Heathcliff which is the basis of Emily Brontë's *Wuthering Heights*. Heathcliff is a foundling gypsy boy brought home by Mr Earnshaw to his family, but after his death the youngster is brutalised by the humiliations heaped on him. His love for Cathy is the one thing that sustains him as a child and an adolescent and when she, for misguided social reasons, decides to marry Edgar Linton, Heathcliff is set upon an inexorable search for revenge. Cathy is a wonderful study of teenage girlish wilfulness and wayward behaviour and Heathcliff of male stubborn mulish reaction. Their deep attachment, however, is shown by their ability in early years to forget any punishment the minute they are together and by the continuation of their adult passion despite all vicissitudes.

Teenagers are capable of suffering acute embarrassment in relation to their peer group. Pip, the hero of Dickens' *Great Expectations*, looking back on his childhood and adolescence from an adult viewpoint, feels shame at his rejection of his simple, good, but poorly educated mentor Joe Gangery because his manners were not likely to find favour with his smart London friends. Writing of the change from childhood to adolescence in her novel *The Mill on the Floss*, George Eliot contrasts the straightforward emotions of childhood with teenage shyness. Describing the adolescent Maggie's inhibitions at kissing her childhood friend Philip she writes, 'the promise was void like so many other sweet illusory promises of our childhood – impossible to be fulfilled when the golden gate had been passed.' Reflecting on Maggie's teenage feelings, faced with her domineering brother, her dependent father and capricious self-centred mother, George Eliot writes, 'There is no hopelessness so sad as that of early youth, when the soul is made up of wants and has no long memories, no superadded life of others.'

In 1885 the French novelist Emile Zola published *Germinal,* an account of life in a mining village, and a novel which perceives the vices and virtues of both the oppressed workers and those who managed and owned the mines. Here we meet Catherine, a teenager working down the mines and, in many ways, a true working-class heroine. She is 15 and not very big 'because girls do not grow very fast hereabouts'. Indeed, she is so poorly developed that she has not begun to menstruate, which is not uncommon where there is anaemia and malnutrition. She is seduced and submits to the alternation of brutal beating and repentant caresses by her lover, because she fears the even worse alternative of a life of prostitution which awaited many girls who found themselves without food and lodging, as it still does today. Despite her privations, however, she remains a strong and caring person, capable of retaining idealistic values.

Teenagers have become more rebellious in this century, both in life and in literature. Graham Greene's Pinky in *Brighton Rock* is a boy gangster in pre-war Brighton. He was brought up as a Catholic, leading him to choose a perverted preoccupation with evil and damnation and a fear and repulsion of normal sexuality which dominates his behaviour. This fascinating study of how psychopathy develops also introduces Rose, aged 16, whose innocence, love and simple goodness is contrasted with Pinky's wickedness. In the end, after Pinky's death, she goes hopefully to hear a message of love on a recording that he has made. She does not realise that she will hear the worst horror of all, the final venom of a psychopath telling her that he hates her.

The Catcher in the Rye by J. D. Salinger was published in 1951 and is written in the first person in the idiom of a 16-year-old New York boy. It is a study which portrays with acute observations and sympathetic insight the motivations of a mixed-up teenager who has run away from home.

A Clockwork Orange by Anthony Burgess, written in 'nadsat', a special teenage type of news-speak, charts the gratuitous violence of 15-year-old Alex and his three friends.

Because of his behaviour, Alex is jailed and subjected to the Ludovico Technique of Reclamation Therapy, a form of deconditioning intended to cure him of his criminal tendencies. One of the issues raised by the book is whether such a treatment is not as violent as Alex's own behaviour, in that it is an attempt to deprive him of the ability to choose between right and wrong. In the end, Alex realises that he is growing up and no longer wishes to be violent. He reflects that being young is like being a Malenky machine which bangs straight into things heedless of what it is doing, and that, when he has a son, he will have difficulty, no matter how hard he explains, in stopping him making the mistakes that he has made.

Literature for teenagers has become a large market. Originally, books for teenagers contained moral homilies about loyalty to the school and conforming to the rules of society. They reflected little of the dark side of life as a teenager such as bullying, unhappiness at home, or parental death or separation. They certainly never dealt with sexual problems or pregnancy. In the past two decades or so, however, authors writing for adolescents have attempted to portray a more realistic picture of life and of the decisions that a young person may have to make.

Adrian Mole, in Sue Townsend's *Diary of Adrian Mole, Aged 13³/4*, must be the archetypal teenager of today. Adrian worries about his spots, about the size of various parts of his anatomy, about his parents and their marriage, and about his appeal or lack of it to the opposite sex, especially the lovely Pandora. Daringly taking an experimental sniff of glue as he assembles his model aeroplane, his nose gets stuck to the plane, he requires treatment in casualty and is labelled a glue sniffer by the doctor. His running away from home is marred by the fact that the family pet dog insists on accompanying him. He rings the Samaritans in despair about his maths homework, only to be given the wrong answer to his problem. He seriously contemplates being a tramp provided he can have regular baths, considers the overthrow of society and his power over women and writes to well-known people asking how to become an intellectual. A teenager's life is never easy!

GLOSSARY

Amenorrhoea Absence of menstrual periods.

Amphetamines A group of drugs which were previously used mainly because of their control of appetite. They have a transitory stimulant effect which is often followed by a rebound depression. They are habit-forming and can produce a paranoid delusional illness.

Anorexia nervosa A condition, most usually found in girls, in which there is severe starvation and weight loss produced by the person's belief, despite being of average weight, that they are excessively fat.

Anxiety A feeling of uneasiness, as if something unpleasant is about to happen.

Bulimia A condition in which periods of binge-eating alternate with self-induced vomiting and laxative abuse.

Cannabis An addictive drug made from the *cannabis sativa* plant.

Chromosomes Rod-like structures found in pairs in all the cells of the body, carrying the genetic determiners (genes) that are transmitted from parent to offspring. A human cell has 46 chromosomes, arranged in 23 pairs, one member of each pair deriving from the mother, one from the father.

Cocaine A powerful drug of addiction made from the leaves of the Andean cocoa shrub.

Crush Intense emotional attachments to unattainable individuals.

Delusion A fixed false belief which cannot be altered by any appeal to logic or reasoning and which is alien to the individual's cultural background and intelligence.

Depression A feeling of profound sadness or in more severe cases a complete loss of interest, often accompanied by physical symptoms such as poor sleep and loss of appetite.

Diabetes A condition in which, due to a lack of insulin (a hormone produced in the pancreas), the body cannot deal with sugar.

Dialysis A process used to purify the blood of waste products when the kidneys, which usually perform this function, are unable to do so.

Endocrine glands Those glands that produce hormones, e.g. pituitary, thyroid, ovary, testicle.

Epilepsy A condition in which irregular patterns in the electric waves of the brain can lead to fits and other symptoms.

Fertilisation The union of an egg cell from the ovary with the spermatozoa from the testes.

Gene The basic unit of hereditary transmission localised within the chromosomes. Each chromosome contains many genes. Genes are typically in pairs, one member of the pair being found in the chromosome from the father, the other being the corresponding chromosome from the mother.

Hallucination A false perception of something which is not present in reality in the external world.

Hallucinogenic Describes a substance which produces halluci-nations.

Hereditary Transmitted from one generation to another by means of the genes.

Heterosexuality Sexual feeling for, and attachment to, a member of the opposite sex.

Homosexuality Sexual feeling for, and attachment to, a member of the same sex.

Hormones Chemical messengers secreted by the endocrine glands into the bloodstream to act upon a target organ, e.g. the pituitary gland in the brain secretes gonadotrophins which act upon the ovaries or testes.

Hypnotics Drugs used to induce sleep.

Intelligence The sum total of an individual's mental abilities.

Karyotype The appearance (size, shape, and number) of the chromosomes.

Menarche The onset of menstrual periods.

Mental handicap A condition where there is impaired develop-ment of the mind associated with a failure to develop normal intelligence.

Obesity The condition of being overweight.

Obsession A persistent thought or act which an individual is unable to fight against, e.g. a constant desire to wash the hands.

Opiates Drugs such as morphine and codeine used in medicine for their pain-killing properties, but also powerful drugs of addiction.

Ovulation The discharge of an egg cell from the ovary into the fallopian tubes.

Phobia Anxiety attached to one particular object or situation.

Pituitary An endocrine hormone-secreting organ at the base of the brain which controls the other endocrine organs such as the thyroid, adrenals, ovary, and testes.

Puberty The period when growth and maturation of the sex organs is initiated, secondary sexual characteristics develop, and sexual fertility is attained.

Psychotherapy Discussion and exploration of the reasons behind an individual's behaviour.

Schizophrenia A psychiatric condition in which there is a disturbance of thinking and emotion, often accompanied by delusions and hallucinations.

Spermatogenesis The development of spermatozoa in the testes.

Stammering Difficulty in pronouncing consonants such as 'b', 'g', 's', and 't'.

Tics Repetitive movements, particularly of the facial muscles.

Tranquillisers Drugs such as Valium or Librium used to control anxiety and tension.

FURTHER READING

Atkins, Carol, *Seeing Red*, André Deutsch. Written by actress turned psychotherapist who looks after over 25 disturbed children and teenagers in two houses in Berkshire and Gloucestershire.

Ballard, J.G., *Empire of the Sun*, Gollancz. Novel about how a teenager copes with life in a Japanese internment camp.

Bromwich, P. and Parsons, T., *Contraception: The Facts*, Oxford University Press.

Brontë, E. *Wuthering Heights*, Penguin.

Burgess, Anthony, *A Clockwork Orange*, Penguin.

Carter, F. and Cheesman, P., *Anxiety in Childhood and Adolescence: Encouraging Self-Help through Relaxation Therapy*, Croom Helm.

Chadwick, D. and Usiskin, S., *Living With Epilepsy*, Macdonald Optima.

Chapman, E., *Visually Handicapped Children and Young People*, Routledge & Kegan Paul.

Collins, S., *Step-Parents and Their Children*, Souvenir Press.

Davenport, D., *One-Parent Families*, Sheldon Press.

Dickens, C., *Great Expectations*, Penguin.

Donaldson, John, *Living With Asthma and Hay Fever*, Penguin.

Drug Problems – Where to Get Help, Scoda National Directory, BBC Publications.

Eliot, George, *The Mill on the Floss*, Penguin.

Greene, Graham, *Brighton Rock*, Penguin.

Hadden, C. and Thomson, P., *Stronger Love: Safer Sex*, Macmillan.

Hardy, Thomas, *Tess of the D'Urbervilles*, Penguin.

Hazeldine, P., *Epilepsy – A Life Crisis*, Thorsons.

Hodder, E., *The Step-Parents' Handbook*, Sphere.

Hornsby, Beve, *Overcoming Dyslexia*, Macdonald Optima.

James, Henry, *What Maisie Knew*, Penguin.

Lintner, Brenda, *Living With Schizophrenia*, Macdonald Optima.

Murray, David, *The Anti-Acne Book*, Arlington Books.

North, Judith, *Teenage Diabetes*, Thorsons.

Priest, R., *Anxiety and Depression*, Macdonald Optima.

Rapport, Judith, *The Boy Who Couldn't Stop Washing*, Collins. The experience and treatment of obsessive compulsive disorder.

Salinger, J.D., *The Catcher in the Rye*, Penguin.

Townsend, S., *The Secret Diary of Adrian Mole aged 13³⁄₄*; *The Growing Pains Of Adrian Mole*, Methuen.

Wesley, Mary, *A Sensible Life*, Guild Publishing. How a young girl copes with parental rejection.

Zola, Emile, *Germinal*, Penguin.

USEFUL ADDRESSES

ABC (Anti-Bullying Campaign)
c/o Kidscape
82 Brook St
London W1Y 1YG
071-493 9845

Al-Ateen
61 Great Dover Street
London SE1 4YF
071-403 0888
Support and help for young people aged 12–20 with an alcoholic relative.

Albany Trust Counselling
24 Chester Square
London SW1W 9HS
071-730 5871
Counselling for all types of sexual identity and relationship problems, with branches in other cities and with literature available.

Alcohol Concern
305 Gray's Inn Road
London WC1X 8QF
071-833 3471

Alcohol Counselling Service
34 Electric Lane
London SW9 8JT
071-737 3579

British Diabetic Association
10 Queen Anne Street
London W1M 0BD
071-323 1531

British Dyslexia Association
Church Lane
Peppard
Oxfordshire RG9 5JN

British Epilepsy Association
Crowthorne House
Bigshotte
New Wokingham Road
Wokingham
Berkshire RG11 3AY
0344 773122

British Pregnancy Advisory Service (Head Office)
Austy Manor
Wootton Wawen
Solihull
West Midlands B95 6BX
056 42 3225

Brook Advisory Centres
233 Tottenham Court Road
London W1P 9AE
071-580 2991 (appointments)
071-323 1522 (information)
Offer information and practical help to anyone concerned
about pregnancy, contraception, or psychosexual problems.
Branches in other cities.

Cancerlink
17 Britannia St
London WC1X 9JN
071-833 2451

Childline
Freepost 1111
London M1 0BR
0800 1111 (Freephone)
A free advice line to help children and young people suffering
violence, neglect or sexual abuse.

Compassionate Friends
6 Denmark Street
Bristol BS1 5DQ
0272 292778
Support and help for people suffering the loss of a child, with many groups throughout Britain.

Cruse
Cruse House
126 Sheen Road
Richmond
Surrey TW9 1UR
081-940 4818
Counselling service with more than 100 branches throughout the UK offering help to widows, widowers, and their children.

Eating Disorders Association
Sackville Place
44 Magdalen Street
Norwich NR3 1JE
0603 621414
Advice, information and support for those suffering from or concerned with anorexia or bulimia.

Fair (Family Action Information and Rescue)
BCM Box 3535
P.O. Box 12,
London WC1N 3XX
081-539 3940
For parents who are worried about their children's involvement with a cult.

Family Planning Association
St Andrew's House
27/35 Mortimer Street
London W1N 7RJ
071-636 7866
Nationwide advice about contraception for young people. Ring above number for local NHS services.

Friends for the Young Deaf Trust
FYD Communication Centre
East Court Mansion
Council Offices
College Lane
East Grinstead
Sussex RH19 3LT
0342 23444
Offers help for young deaf people in the community.

Gingerbread
35 Wellington Street
London WC2E 7BN
071-240 0953
Self-help groups for one-parent families.

Health Education Authority
Hamilton House
Mabledon Place
London WC1H 9TX
071-383 3833
Free information on a very wide range of health topics including those relating to teenagers.

Institute for the Study of Drug Dependence
1–4 Hatton Place
Hatton Garden
London EC1N 8ND
071-430-1991
Information about drugs, excluding alcohol and tobacco.

Invalid Children's Aid Association
126 Buckingham Palace Road
London SW1W 9SB
071-730 9891
Free help and advice for parents with handicapped children.

Lesbian and Gay Switchboard
071-837 7324 (24-hour)

MENCAP
123 Golden Lane
London EC1Y 0RT
071-253 9433
Practical help, advice, support, and information for the mentally handicapped and their families.

MIND (National Association for Mental Health)
22 Harley Street
London W1N 2ED
071-637 0741
Offers advice about all aspects of mental health.

National Association for Gifted Children
1 South Audley Street
London W1Y 5DQ
071-499 1188

National Association of Young People's Counselling and Advisory Services
17–23 Albion Street
Leicester LE1 6GD
0533 558763
Advises about local services including counselling, information and befriending.

National Asthma Campaign
300 Upper Street
London N1 2XX

National Bureau for Students With Disabilities
336 Brixton Road
London SW9 7AA
071-274 0565
Information and advice service on education in all types of handicap.

National Campaign Against Solvent Abuse
Box 513
245a Coldharbour Lane
London SW9 8RR
071-733 7330
24-hour help-line for those abusing solvents (e.g. glue sniffers)

National Council for One-Parent Families
255 Kentish Town Road
London NW5 2LX
071-267 1361

National Kidney Research Fund
42 Lower Marsh
London SE1 7RJ
071-928 5058
Information about kidney problems.

National Schizophrenia Fellowship
28 Castle Street
Kingston-upon-Thames
Surrey KT1 1SS
081-547 3937

National Stepfamily Association
162 Tenison Rd
Cambridge
CB1 2DP
0223 460313

OPUS (Organisation for Parents under Stress)
106 Godstone Road
Whyteleaf
Surrey CR3 0EB
081-645 0469
Self-help group with many branches for parents under stress.

Prince of Wales Youth Business Trust
5 The Pavement
London SW4 0HY
Helps unemployed youngsters to start off in business.

Psychotherapy Centre
67 Upper Berkeley Street
London W1H 7DH
071-262 8852
Advice about obtaining psychotherapeutic help.

Release
169 Commercial St
London E1 6BW
071-377 5905 (Mon-Fri, 10-6)
071-603 8654 (all other times)
Advice and information, referral and counselling on drug-related problems, including legal.

Spinal Injuries Association
Yeoman House
76 St James's Lane
London N10 3DF
081-444 2121
Link scheme whereby someone who has had a spinal injury will
visit and befriend a newly injured person.

Stepfamily
72 Willesden Lane
London NW6 7TA
071-372 0844
Supplies lists of counsellors and self-help groups.

Vegetarian Society (Youth Information)
Parkdale
Dunham Road
Altrincham
Cheshire WA14 4QG
061-928 0793

INDEX

124

LSD, 65–6, 67, 87
luteinising hormone (LH), 2
lying, 72–3

Macmillan nurses, 92
magic mushrooms, 67–8
magistrates, 77
marijuana, 65
marriage: arranged marriages,
    102, 103; divorce, 24–5; 92;
    separation, 22; stepfamilies,
    22–3; teenage marriages, 46
masturbation, 105
memory, 30, 65
menstruation: 73; absence of, 4,
    38, 40; anaemia, 28; onset of,
    1, 2–3, 43
mental ability, 26
mental handicap, 82–3
mental illness, 84–9
The Mill on the Floss, 108–9
minerals, 34, 36, 40
More, Lady Margaret, 104
More, Sir Thomas, 104
'morning after pill', 46
morphine, 66
mushrooms, magic, 67–8
music, 30
mutilation, 75
My Left Foot, 82

National Stepfamily Association,
    23
nembutal, 64
Nicholas Nickleby, 105
nicotine, 60–1
nightmares, 17
novels, teenagers in, 107–10
nutrition, 3–4, 33–8

obesity, 33, 35–8
obsessions, 18–19
oestradiol, 2
oestrogen, 45–6
opiates, 66–7
oral contraceptives, 45
ovaries, 1, 2, 4
overdoses, drug, 69
overprotectiveness, 8–9, 16

ovulation, 2, 45–6

pancreas, fibrocystic disease, 4
paralysis, 82
parents: attitudes, 11–13, 16;
    relationships, 21–2;
    step-parents, 22–3
parties, 62–3
penis, 1
periods *see* menstruation
personality, 19, 21
phobias, 16–18
physical disability, 81–2
physiological changes, 1–6
pill, contraceptive, 45
pituitary gland, 1–2, 4
plays, teenagers in, 107
police, 77
polytechnics, 31, 97–9, 100
pop stars, 44, 55, 56
pornography, 49
post-traumatic stress disorder,
    17–18
pregnancy, 43, 45, 46–7, 69, 73,
    105–6
progesterone, 2–3, 45–6
promiscuity, 76
prostitution, 76, 104
protein, 33–4
psychiatric illness, 84–9
psychiatrists, 78
psychological factors: changes in
        puberty, 5; delayed puberty,
        4; learning difficulties, 28–9;
        and obesity, 36
psychologists, educational, 27
psychosis, drug, 64, 66
puberty: delayed, 3–5
    physiological changes, 1–6
pubic hair, 1
pubs, 61
punishment, at school, 58–9

Rantzen, Esther, 48
Rattigan, Terence, 58
rebellion, 8–9
Red Guard, 105
regulations, school, 59
road accidents, 61, 90, 93–4

127

universities, 31, 96, 97–9, 100

valium, 63, 70
values, questioning of, 8
vegetables, 33
vegetarianism, 35
venereal disease, 43, 104
videos, sexual violence, 49
violence, 49, 75–6
viral illnesses, 20
vitamins, 34, 36
vomiting, 39–40

warfare, 105
weight reduction, 35–8
What Maisie Knew, 108
withdrawal, schizophrenia, 87
withdrawal method,
   contraception, 46
womb, menstruation, 3
Wordsworth, William, 107
work, 82, 99–101, 104
Wuthering Heights, 108

Zola, Emile, 109

MORE BOOKS FROM OPTIMA

POSITIVE HEALTH GUIDES

Diabetes – A Young Person's Guide by Dr Rowan Hillson

Learning to live with diabetes and enjoying life to the full is helped by knowing more about the condition. The book describes some young people's experiences and how their diabetes affected them.

Dr Rowan Hillson, Consultant Endocrinologist at Hillingdon, has written a practical and reassuring guide which covers:

- Diagnosis, symptoms and treatment
- Food, weight control and exercise
- Relationships and sex
- School, college and university
- Leaving home
- Starting work
- Holidays and travelling

ISBN 0 356 15415 7
Price (in UK only) £5.99

Overcoming Dyslexia by Dr Bevé Hornsby

Dyslexia is commonly defined as a difficulty in learning to read and write, because it is at this stage of a child's development that the problem becomes most obvious. But what is it, and how can parents and teachers help their children?

Dr Bevé Hornsby combines her experience as a psychologist, teacher and speech therapist to specialise in helping children with dyslexia. She has written this excellent book for them, their families and schools in order that the problems of dyslexia can be understood and tackled successfully.

'This easy-to-read book is optimistic and full of practical advice ... no teacher or parent or dyslexic child should be without it.'

Susan Hampshire

ISBN 0 356 14499 2
Price (in UK only) £5.99

OTHER BOOKS FROM OPTIMA

Answers to Acne by Dr Gillian Murphy

- Why have I got acne?
- What can I do about it?
- What help can my doctor offer?
- What are the latest treatments?
- Could antibiotics help me?
- What about herbal medicine or homeopathy?
- Should I change my diet?
- Is there anything else I can do?

The book provides a complete rundown of the different treatments for acne in conventional and alternative medicine, and also self-help, analysing the benefits and pitfalls of each. With its positive and practical approach, it is an indispensable reference for all acne sufferers.

The author, Dr Gillian Murphy, specializes in the treatment of skin problems and is Senior Registrar at St John's Hospital for Diseases of the Skin.

ISBN 0 356 12434 7
Price (in UK only) £3.95

Stepfamilies Talking by Elizabeth Hodder

'The trouble with stepfamilies is that the adults behave like children but expect the children to behave like adults.'

In Britain alone six million people belong to stepfamilies and numbers are increasing. The formation of a new family creates a whole range of problems. How do readymade mothers, fathers, sons and daughters handle jealousy, guilt and insecurity? And do they ever come to enjoy a rewarding sense of family unity?

Elizabeth Hodder – founder and co-director of the National Stepfamily Association – has posed these questions to ten families of different backgrounds and circumstances. Her honest, direct approach will prove enlightening to all those who feel isolated, threatened or challenged by the stresses and strains of stepfamily life.

ISBN 0 356 15642 7
Price (in UK only) £4.99

Green Parenting by Juliet Solomon

The awakening of Green consciousness has provoked much discussion about saving the planet for future generations, but the importance of today's children has received little attention. How might Green parents raise their daughters and sons to be Green?

Green Parenting presents thought provoking ways to bring up children and to avoid the pressures of consumerism and commercialism that surround children and their parents. Linking the work of Green thinkers and child psychologists, and covering practical areas such as health and diet, education, games and entertainment, and attitudes to children, it offers rewarding and refreshing alternatives for everyone involved with children, whether they aspire to be Green or not.

ISBN 0 356 18768 3
Price (in UK only) £6.99

Phobias by Joy Melville

- agoraphobia
- terror of spiders
- fear of flying
- school phobia
- claustrophobia
- animal phobias
- fear of illness
- horror of needles
- fear of heights

The number of phobics and the extent of their fears has long been unacknowledged. It is possible to have a phobia about almost anything, and in this book Joy Melville examines an astonishing range of familiar and rare phobias which are known and can be treated.

Phobias will reassure phobics that they are not isolated by their fears and will help to show how different phobias and obsessions can be treated. Joy Melville also outlines self-help methods and offers advice that will help both the phobic and friends and relatives to cope with the problems caused by a phobia.

ISBN 0 356 20238 0
Price (in UK only) £6.99
(Published in June 1991)

Children's Problems by Dr Bryan Lask

From tantrums to truancy, from bedwetting to food fads, this book looks at the emotional, behavioural and developmental problems children may experience (and parents may suffer) from infancy to adolescence.

Dr Bryan Lask, Consultant Child Psychiatrist at the world-famous Hospital for Sick Children, Great Ormond St, draws upon over twenty years of experience as he:

● distinguishes between a serious problem and a normal 'going through a phase'
● looks at causes, practical solutions and treatments, with case histories and step-by-step sequences for managing common problems
● outlines the role of parents in setting an example, being consistent and flexible and giving rewards and punishments

'remarkable for two reasons; absence of psychological jargon and a commonsense approach' *British Medical Journal*

ISBN 0 356 19773 5
Price (in UK only) £6.99

Get a Better Night's Sleep by Professor Ian Oswald and Dr Kirstine Adam

● Problems getting to sleep?
● Worried your sleep isn't as good as it should be?

In this practical and sympathetic guide, sleep experts Professor Ian Oswald and Dr Kirstine Adam help people with insomnia to achieve a more restful night's sleep. They identify the causes of broken sleep, insomnia and nightmares and show how nicotine and alcohol, poor diet, inadequate exercise and irregular hours affect the quality of your sleep. Their practical, scientifically based advice offers the best ways to avoid sleeplessness and wake refreshed every morning.

'A riveting book for a non-medical audience.' *Observer*

ISBN 0 356 19674 7
Price (in UK only) £5.99

Healthy Feet by Lewis Russell FChS, SRCh and Bob Hardy MSSF

By the time we are 70, most of us will have walked an estimated 75,000 miles, our feet taking the strain. Care of the feet should be a priority, but often they are neglected and abused.

Healthy Feet combines the expertise of a chiropodist and a shoe fitter to provide comprehensive information on all aspects of foot care. Illustrated throughout, the book covers

- Basic foot anatomy and physiology
- Primary footcare
- Common foot complaints
- Importance of correct shoe fitting
- Care of children's feet
- Older feet
- Diabetic feet
- Footcare for sports enthusiasts

ISBN 0 356 15190 5
Price (in UK only) £5.99

Ears and Hearing by Michael Martin OBE and Brian Grover

The ability to hear is often taken for granted, but it plays a vital part in human communication. Distress and misunderstanding may, therefore, face those contending with deafness or impaired hearing.

In *Ears and Hearing*, Michael Martin OBE and Brian Grover of the Royal National Institute for the Deaf dispel the ignorance and misconceptions surrounding deafness by providing comprehensive information and practical advice on:

- How we hear
- Causes of hearing loss
- Prevention and treatment
- Deafness in children
- Hearing aids and other aids
- Overcoming problems of communication
- Help available from professionals and voluntary organisations

ISBN 0 356 17234 1
Price (in UK only) £5.99

Sex Problems: Your Questions Answered by Martin Cole and Windy Dryden

Written by two highly experienced therapists in response to the need for a comprehensive book on the subject that they could recommend to those seeking help, SEX PROBLEMS presents the facts about sex and sex therapy in a readable, accessible style.

Questions answered include many of general interest, for example those concerning frequency of intercourse or the average size of an erect penis, as well as questions concerning specific problems, for example with orgasm, erection, premature ejaculation and lack of sexual interest. A chapter is also included on sex offenders and the law.

All the information is clearly presented in a question-and-answer format, a unique feature for this type of book, enabling the reader to find any information they want quickly and easily.

ISBN 0 356 15985 X
Price (in UK only) £4.99

The Future is Now by Deidre Rhys-Thomas

'The greatest danger to the planet Earth is the existence of the animal man.' *Tom Conti*

'Nobody can be proud of the fact that the Irish Sea is a dustbin, and I think it's absolutely tragic that Britain has refused to stop the dumping of sewage sludge into the North Sea.' *Stanley Clinton Davies*

'We continue to use pesticides which are not used anywhere else in the world anymore. They have been forbidden elsewhere.' *Igor Shabdurqulov*

'The opinion polls are very clear. Between 65 and 70 per cent of the people in this country do not want any expansion in the nuclear power programme.' *Jonathon Porritt*

In these frank and illuminating interviews, MICHAEL ASPEL, PAMELA STEPHENSON, DAVID PUTTNAM, EMMA THOMPSON, CLIVE PONTING, TOM JONES and CLAIRE RAYNER are among people from both sides of the Iron Curtain in the media, the arts, public affairs, science and health professions who voice their concerns about the environmental dangers facing our planet.

ISBN 0 356 17947 8
Price (in UK only) £4.99

All Optima books are available at your bookshop or newsagent, or can be ordered from the following address:

Optima Books
Cash Sales Department
PO Box 11
Falmouth
Cornwall TR10 9EN

Alternatively you may fax your order to the above address. Fax number: 0326 76423

Payments can be made as follows: Cheque, postal order (payable to Macdonald & Co (Publishers) Ltd) or by credit cards, Visa/Access. *Do not send cash or currency.*

UK customers, please send a cheque or postal order (no currency) and allow 80p for postage and packing for the first book plus 20p for each additional book up to a maximum charge of £2.00.

BFPO customers, please allow 80p for the first book plus 20p for each additional book.

Overseas customers, including Ireland, please allow £1.50 for postage and packing for the first book, £1.00 for the second book and 30p for each additional book.

NAME (Block letters) ....

ADDRESS ....

....

    I enclose my remittance for _____

    I wish to pay by Access/Visa Card

Number ☐☐☐☐☐☐☐☐☐☐☐☐☐☐☐☐

Card expiry date